DREAMLAND

MENTAL MATHEMATICS

BOOK 2

by:

T. Raaj Bhanot

Published by

DREAMLAND PUBLICATIONS

J-128, KIRTI NAGAR, NEW DELHI-110 015 (INDIA)

PHONE : 011- 2510 6050, FAX : 011- 2543 8283

E-mail : dreamland@vsnl.com

Shop online at www.dreamlandpublications.com

Published in 2015 by
Dreamland Publications
J-128, Kirti Nagar, New Delhi- 110 015 (India)
Tel.: 011-2510 6050, Fax : 011-2543 8283

ISBN 978-93-5089-189-6

PREFACE

The present series—DREAMLAND MENTAL MATHEMATICS— aims at serving as an active guide to teachers and students for acquiring quick methods of calculations. These methods are bound to be useful not only during the school-stage but in practical life also when the students have grown up to enter life.

The handy tips about calculations are sure to sharpen the intellectual capacity of the learners—a capacity that is a must in the fast-changing life-styles of today. Men with sharp brain are in high demand almost in every walk of life. Tough competition in every field calls for brain with brawn indeed.

The present book is meant for children of age-group 6+ which corresponds to standard I of the primary schools. It deals with—

- 3-digit Numerals ; Their Formation
- 3-digit Numerals ; Their Addition and Subtraction
- Ascending Order and Descending Order
- Multiplication As Repeated Addition
- Division As Repeated Subtraction
- Division Using Multiplication Tables
- Angles and Triangles
- Quadrilaterals

We feel highly delighted while placing this series in the hands of the teachers and taught with a positive hope that it will meet their approval admirably. It is certainly a series with a difference. Still no human work can claim to be flawless. So constructive suggestions for the betterment of the series shall be welcomed to be incorporated in the coming edition if found up to the mark.

—PUBLISHERS

CONTENTS

① WHAT WE ALREADY KNOW

A. Fill up each blank :

1. Numbers 0 to 9 are called _Units_ .
2. Numbers 10 to 19 are called _tens_ .
3. Numbers 20 to 29 are called _1 twenties_ .
4. Numbers 30 to 39 are called _thirties_ .
5. Numbers 40 to 49 are called _fourties_ .
6. Numbers 50 to 59 are called _fifties_ .
7. Numbers 60 to 69 are called _sixties_ .
8. Numbers 70 to 79 are called _seventies_ .
9. Numbers 80 to 89 are called _eighties_ .
10. Numbers 90 to 99 are called _nineties_ .

B. Solve the following sums by break-up method :

☐ 15 − 8 = _10_ + _5_ − _8_ = _3_ + _4_ = | _7_ |
☐ 9 + 7 = _10_ + _4_ + _2_ = _90_ + _15_ = | _16_ |
☐ 25 + 9 = _20_ + _5_ + _9_ = _30_ + _4_ = | _34_ |
☐ 56 − 7 = _50_ + _6_ − _7_ = _39_ + _10_ = | _49_ |
☐ 64 − 8 = _60_ + _4_ − _8_ = _5_ + _51_ = | _56_ |

C. Answer the following :

1. How many ones does 9 stand for ? _Nine_
2. How many digits are used to write a ten ? _two_
3. Which number is the highest ten ? _90_
4. How many tens are there in a forty ? _4_
5. What do we get by adding 1 to 59 ? _60_
6. What does the digit 6 show in 68 ? _6 tens_
7. What does the digit 8 show in 68 ? _8 ones_

D. Solve the following sums mentally :

▫ 4 + 3 + 2 = **9**

▫ 8 – 3 = **5**

▫ 5 + 8 + 4 = **17**

▫ 29 – 4 – 3 = **22**

▫ 37 + 7 + 5 = **49** =7×7

▫ 67 – 5 – 1 = **61**

E. Write the correct numeral in each blank :

▫ 1 kilogram = __**5**__ weights of 200 g each.

▫ 1 litre = __**2**__ vessels of 500 ml/mL each.

▫ Lines can be of __**3**__ types : straight, curved, zig-zag.

▫ Straight lines are of __**3**__ types : vertical, horizontal, slanting.

▫ A triangle has __**2**__ slanting and __**1**__ horizontal sides.

▫ A circle is made up of only __**1**__ curved line.

F. Name the shape under each picture :

CUbeoid

Sphere

cube

Cone

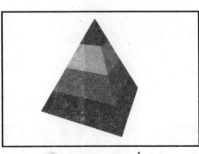
pyramid

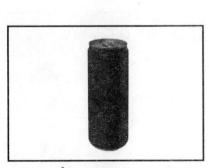
cylinder

② 3-DIGIT NUMERALS

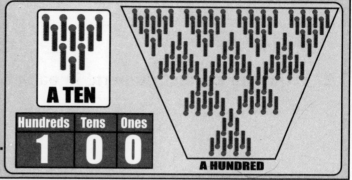

A TEN

Hundreds	Tens	Ones
1	0	0

A HUNDRED

DO YOURSELF

A. Write the correct number against each picture :

100 + 30 + 4 = 134

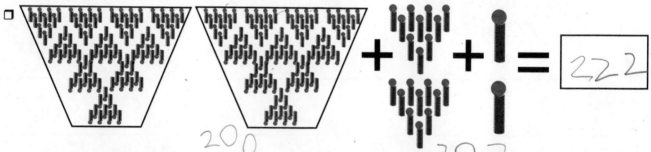

200 + 202 = 222

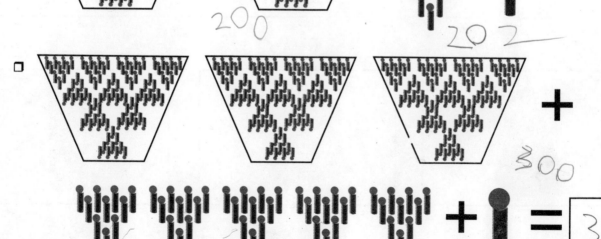

300 + 351

6

B. Write—

- The lowest 1-digit number = 1
- The highest 1-digit number = 9
- The lowest 2-digit number = 10
- The highest 2-digit number = 99
- The lowest 3-digit number = 100
- The highest 3-digit number = 999

C. Write the correct numeral in each blank :

- Three hundred and forty two _____ 342
- Eight hundred and two _____ 802
- Five hundred and thirty-five _____ 535
- One hundred and fifty-one _____ 151
- Six hundred and twenty-three _____ 623
- Seven hundred and sixty-nine _____ 769
- Four hundred and forty-seven _____ 447
- Two hundred and thirty-four _____ 234
- Nine hundred and fifty-four _____ 954

D. Write each numeral in words :

- 441 = Four hundred forty one
- 837 = eight hundred thirty seven
- 753 = seven hundred fifty three
- 349 = three hundred fourty ~~the~~ nine
- 923 = nine hundred twenty three
- 503 = five hundred three
- 634 = six hundred thirty four
- 782 = seven hundred eighty two
- 550 = five hundred fifty

③ FORMING 3-DIGIT NUMERALS

- If we are to form all possible numerals using the digits **1, 2, 3,** we shall place 1 in the hundred's place and the other two digits as tens and ones in turn to form two numerals.

123	**132**
213	**231**
312	**321**

  We shall repeat the process with **2** in the hundred's place to form another two numerals.

  We shall again repeat the process with **3** in the hundred's place to form still another two numerals.

- Thus we shall make six numerals in all.

- **123** is the lowest numeral of all and **321** is the highest one.

- To form the **lowest numeral**, write the digits in ascending order. To form the **highest numeral**, write the digits in descending order.

DO YOURSELF

A. Make six possible numbers with each set of digits :

❐   5, 8, 7

❐   6, 0, 9

❐   7, 6, 3

❐   1, 9, 8

□ 6, 7, 8

□ 4, 2, 0

B. Write the **lowest** and the **highest numbers** formed with each set of digits :

Digits	Lowest Numeral	Highest Numeral
□ 6, 5, 2		
□ 4, 1, 3		
□ 7, 8, 6		
□ 3, 1, 4		
□ 4, 1, 2		
□ 5, 0, 3		
□ 7, 8, 9		
□ 5, 1, 6		

C. Observe the example and write the place value of the digit in colour :

In 435,   place value of 4 = 4 hundreds   = 400
            place value of 3 = 3 tens   = 30
            place value of 5 = 5 units   =   5

Numeral	Place value	Numeral	Place value
□ 456 =	_____	□ 329 =	_____
□ 646 =	_____	□ 492 =	_____
□ 503 =	_____	□ 704 =	_____
□ 936 =	_____	□ 278 =	_____

4 ADDING ONES TO 3-DIGIT NUMERALS—I

READ CAREFULLY

- Numerals from 100 to 999 are 3-digit numerals.
- While adding a digit to a 3-digit numeral, break it up into hundreds, tens and ones.
- Then add the given digit to it.

$272 + 5$
$= 200 + 70 + 2 + 5.$
$= 200 + 70 + 7 = 277$
$272 + 5 = 277$

DO YOURSELF

A. Do these sums by **break-up method** :

□ 561 + 7

$500 + 60 + 1 + 7 = 500 + 60 + 8 = \boxed{568}$

□ 823 + 4

_____ + ____ + ____ + ____ = ____ + ____ + ____ = [   ]

□ 690 + 9

_____ + ____ + ____ + ____ = ____ + ____ + ____ = [   ]

□ 765 + 1

_____ + ____ + ____ + ____ = ____ + ____ + ____ = [   ]

□ 435 + 2

_____ + ____ + ____ + ____ = ____ + ____ + ____ = [   ]

□ 652 + 3

_____ + ____ + ____ + ____ = ____ + ____ + ____ = [   ]

□ 881 + 6

_____ + ____ + ____ + ____ = ____ + ____ + ____ = [   ]

B. Solve these sums mentally :

❏ 293 + 6

_____ + _____ + _____ + _____ = _____ + _____ + _____ = [____]

❏ 936 + 2

_____ + _____ + _____ + _____ = _____ + _____ + _____ = [____]

❏ 823 + 4

_____ + _____ + _____ + _____ = _____ + _____ + _____ = [____]

❏ 444 + 5

_____ + _____ + _____ + _____ = _____ + _____ + _____ = [____]

❏ 512 + 6

_____ + _____ + _____ + _____ = _____ + _____ + _____ = [____]

❏ 653 + 5

_____ + _____ + _____ + _____ = _____ + _____ + _____ = [____]

❏ 731 + 4

_____ + _____ + _____ + _____ = _____ + _____ + _____ = [____]

❏ 542 + 6

_____ + _____ + _____ + _____ = _____ + _____ + _____ = [____]

❏ 143 + 1

_____ + _____ + _____ + _____ = _____ + _____ + _____ = [____]

❏ 271 + 6

_____ + _____ + _____ + _____ = _____ + _____ + _____ = [____]

❏ 973 + 5

_____ + _____ + _____ + _____ = _____ + _____ + _____ = [____]

C. Solve the following problems mentally :

□ Mr Brown sold 322 strawberries to one customer and 7 strawberries to another. How many strawberries did he sell in all ?

322 + 7 = 300 + 20 + 2 +7 = $\boxed{329}$

□ There were 784 men in a party. 5 women joined them later on. How many people were there at the party in all ?

_____ + _____ = _____ + _____ + _____ + _____ = $\boxed{}$

□ A baker had 433 eggs. 6 more eggs were laid by his hen. How many eggs had the baker got in all ?

_____ + _____ = _____ + _____ + _____ + _____ = $\boxed{}$

□ Mary bought a toy for $ 516. She had to pay $ 3 as tax on it. How much did Mary pay in all ?

_____ + _____ = _____ + _____ + _____ + _____ = $\boxed{}$

□ Andrew read 142 pages of a book during the day. He read 6 more pages at night. How many pages did he read in all ?

_____ + _____ = _____ + _____ + _____ + _____ = $\boxed{}$

□ A baker sold 521 cookies in the morning and 8 cookies at noon. How many cookies did he sell in all ?

_____ + _____ = _____ + _____ + _____ + _____ = $\boxed{}$

□ A fruit-seller bought 432 oranges from one dealer and 7 oranges from another dealer. How many oranges did he buy in all ?

_____ + _____ = _____ + _____ + _____ + _____ = $\boxed{}$

□ A school had 863 students on April 1. 6 new students got admitted to the school. How many students had the school got in all ?

_____ + _____ = _____ + _____ + _____ + _____ = $\boxed{}$

□ A cart had 952 melons on it. 7 more melons were placed on it. How many melons had the cart got in all ?

_____ + _____ = _____ + _____ + _____ + _____ = $\boxed{}$

□ A marriage-party had 462 guests. 7 new guests joined them. How many guests had the party got in all ?

_____ + _____ = _____ + _____ + _____ + _____ = $\boxed{}$

5 ADDING ONES TO 3-DIGIT NUMERALS—II

- Break up the 3-digit numeral such that it makes a **ten** with the given digit.

- Then add up the ten to get the total.

$$785 + 7$$
$$= 782 + 3 + 7$$
$$= 782 + 10 = 792$$
$$785 + 7 = 792$$

DO YOURSELF

A. Do these sums by break-up method :

❑ 316 + 7

= 313 + 3 + 7 = 313 + 10 = 323

❑ 608 + 4

= _____ + _____ + _____ = _____ + _____ =

❑ 174 + 8

= _____ + _____ + _____ = _____ + _____ =

❑ 323 + 9

= _____ + _____ + _____ = _____ + _____ =

❑ 935 + 6

= _____ + _____ + _____ = _____ + _____ =

❑ 447 + 5

= _____ + _____ + _____ = _____ + _____ =

❑ 279 + 3

= _____ + _____ + _____ = _____ + _____ =

❑ 518 + 2

= _____ + _____ + _____ = _____ + _____ =

B. Solve the following problems mentally :

❑ Pat has 327 marbles. He wins 5 more marbles in a game. How many marbles has he got in all ?

= _____ + _____ + _____ = _____ + _____ = [ ]

❑ There are 609 soldiers in a fort. 2 more soldiers are sent there. How many soldiers has the fort got in all ?

= _____ + _____ + _____ = _____ + _____ = [ ]

❑ A baker bakes 937 biscuits in the first lot. But he has to bake 4 more biscuits for a customer. How many biscuits does he bake in all ?

= _____ + _____ + _____ = _____ + _____ = [ ]

❑ A reader reads 324 pages of a book on Sunday. But on Monday he can read 8 pages only. How many pages does he read in all ?

= _____ + _____ + _____ = _____ + _____ = [ ]

❑ A fruit-seller buys 446 oranges. Later on, he gets 7 more oranges. How many oranges has he got in all ?

= _____ + _____ + _____ = _____ + _____ = [ ]

❑ There were 909 males in a marriage-party. Three women joined in later on. How many people were there in the party in all ?

= _____ + _____ + _____ = _____ + _____ = [ ]

❑ 278 melons were loaded on a camel-cart. 6 more melons were placed on it later on. How many melons had the cart in all ?

= _____ + _____ + _____ = _____ + _____ = [ ]

❑ There were 826 students in a school. 9 new students got admission in that school. How many students had the school got in all ?

= _____ + _____ + _____ = _____ + _____ = [ ]

❑ A garden has 518 trees in it. 2 more trees are planted by the gardener. How many trees are there in the garden in all ?

= _____ + _____ + _____ = _____ + _____ = [ ]

❑ A florist had 316 rose flowers. He bought 7 lotus flowers as well. How many flowers had he got in all ?

= _____ + _____ + _____ = _____ + _____ = [ ]

6 ADDING ONES TO 3-DIGIT NUMERALS—III

- Break up the 3-digit numerals into **hundreds**, **tens** and **ones**.

- Add the tens to tens and ones to ones.

- Finally add up all to get the total.

$549 + 3$
$= 500 + 40 + 9 + 3$
$= 540 + 10 + 2 = 552$

$549 + 3 = 552$

DO YOURSELF

A. Do these sums by break-up method :

❑ $449 + 3$
$= 400 + 40 + 9 + 3 = 400 + 40 + 10 + 2 = \boxed{452}$

❑ $256 + 7$

$= \underline{\hphantom{00}} + \underline{\hphantom{00}} + \underline{\hphantom{00}} + \underline{\hphantom{00}} = \underline{\hphantom{00}} + \underline{\hphantom{00}} + \underline{\hphantom{00}} + \underline{\hphantom{00}} = \boxed{\hphantom{000}}$

❑ $323 + 9$

$= \underline{\hphantom{00}} + \underline{\hphantom{00}} + \underline{\hphantom{00}} + \underline{\hphantom{00}} = \underline{\hphantom{00}} + \underline{\hphantom{00}} + \underline{\hphantom{00}} + \underline{\hphantom{00}} = \boxed{\hphantom{000}}$

❑ $827 + 5$

$= \underline{\hphantom{00}} + \underline{\hphantom{00}} + \underline{\hphantom{00}} + \underline{\hphantom{00}} = \underline{\hphantom{00}} + \underline{\hphantom{00}} + \underline{\hphantom{00}} + \underline{\hphantom{00}} = \boxed{\hphantom{000}}$

❑ $517 + 6$

$= \underline{\hphantom{00}} + \underline{\hphantom{00}} + \underline{\hphantom{00}} + \underline{\hphantom{00}} = \underline{\hphantom{00}} + \underline{\hphantom{00}} + \underline{\hphantom{00}} + \underline{\hphantom{00}} = \boxed{\hphantom{000}}$

❑ $907 + 5$

$= \underline{\hphantom{00}} + \underline{\hphantom{00}} + \underline{\hphantom{00}} + \underline{\hphantom{00}} = \underline{\hphantom{00}} + \underline{\hphantom{00}} + \underline{\hphantom{00}} + \underline{\hphantom{00}} = \boxed{\hphantom{000}}$

❑ $149 + 4$

$= \underline{\hphantom{00}} + \underline{\hphantom{00}} + \underline{\hphantom{00}} + \underline{\hphantom{00}} = \underline{\hphantom{00}} + \underline{\hphantom{00}} + \underline{\hphantom{00}} + \underline{\hphantom{00}} = \boxed{\hphantom{000}}$

❑ $378 + 8$

$= \underline{\hphantom{00}} + \underline{\hphantom{00}} + \underline{\hphantom{00}} + \underline{\hphantom{00}} = \underline{\hphantom{00}} + \underline{\hphantom{00}} + \underline{\hphantom{00}} + \underline{\hphantom{00}} = \boxed{\hphantom{000}}$

B. Solve the following problems mentally :

❏ A cap-seller has 149 caps. He buys 5 more caps. How many caps has he got now in all ?

= _____ + _____ + _____ + _____ = _____ + _____ + _____ + _____ = □

❏ There were 937 eggs with a baker. His hen laid 7 more eggs for him. How many eggs had the baker in all ?

= _____ + _____ + _____ + _____ = _____ + _____ + _____ + _____ = □

❏ There were 298 soldiers in a fort. 3 more soldiers arrived there. How many soldiers had the fort got in all ?

= _____ + _____ + _____ + _____ = _____ + _____ + _____ + _____ = □

❏ Ann bought a dress for $187. She had to pay $ 5 as surcharge also. How much did she spend in all ?

= _____ + _____ + _____ + _____ = _____ + _____ + _____ + _____ = □

❏ A cart was loaded with 438 watermelons. 4 more watermelons were placed on it. How many watermelons were there on the cart in all ?

= _____ + _____ + _____ + _____ = _____ + _____ + _____ + _____ = □

❏ A baker cooks 556 cookies. He has to cook 5 more cookies for a customer. How many cookies did he cook in all ?

= _____ + _____ + _____ + _____ = _____ + _____ + _____ + _____ = □

❏ A shopkeeper bought 376 mangoes from one dealer and 8 mangoes from another dealer. How many mangoes did he buy in all ?

= _____ + _____ + _____ + _____ = _____ + _____ + _____ + _____ = □

❏ A factory has 659 workers in its office. 6 guards are employed for the security of the factory. How many employees has the factory in all ?

= _____ + _____ + _____ + _____ = _____ + _____ + _____ + _____ = □

❏ A big basket has 744 apples in it. 8 more apples were placed in it. How many apples has it got in all ?

= _____ + _____ + _____ + _____ = _____ + _____ + _____ + _____ = □

❏ There were 338 guests at a reception-party. 3 more guests arrived. How many guests had the reception-party in all ?

= _____ + _____ + _____ + _____ = _____ + _____ + _____ + _____ = □

7 ADDING 2-DIGIT AND 3-DIGIT NUMERALS—I

READ CAREFULLY

- Break up a digit from the 3-digit numeral.
- Add this digit to the 2-digit numeral to make a **ten**.
- Add the new ten and the extra digit to the 3-digit numeral to get the total.

$827 + 34$
$= 820 + 7 + 34$
$= 820 + 7 + 33 + 1 =$
$= 820 + 40 + 1 = 861$

$827 + 34 = 861$

DO YOURSELF

A. Do these sums by break-up method :

❑ $763 + 28$
$= 760 + 3 + 28 = 760 + 30 + 1 = 790 + 1 = \boxed{791}$

❑ $164 + 17$

= ____ + ____ + ____ = ____ + ____ + ____ = ____ + ____ = ☐

❑ $527 + 46$

= ____ + ____ + ____ = ____ + ____ + ____ = ____ + ____ = ☐

❑ $226 + 25$

= ____ + ____ + ____ = ____ + ____ + ____ = ____ + ____ = ☐

❑ $465 + 18$

= ____ + ____ + ____ = ____ + ____ + ____ = ____ + ____ = ☐

❑ $636 + 57$

= ____ + ____ + ____ = ____ + ____ + ____ = ____ + ____ = ☐

❑ $731 + 41$

= ____ + ____ + ____ = ____ + ____ + ____ = ____ + ____ = ☐

❑ $802 + 68$

= ____ + ____ + ____ = ____ + ____ + ____ = ____ + ____ = ☐

B. Solve the following problems **mentally** :

❑ A baker bakes 388 biscuits in the first lot and 16 biscuits in the second lot. How many biscuits does he bake in all ?

= _____ + _____ + _____ = _____ + _____ + _____ = _____ + _____ = ☐

❑ A cart has 970 pumpkins loaded on it. 25 more pumpkins are placed on it. How many pumpkins has the cart in all ?

= _____ + _____ + _____ = _____ + _____ + _____ = _____ + _____ = ☐

❑ There were 685 students in a school. 28 more students got admission in that school. How many students had the school got in all ?

= _____ + _____ + _____ = _____ + _____ + _____ = _____ + _____ = ☐

❑ Lucy's mother bought a dress for her paying $ 274. She had to pay $ 17 as surcharge also. How much did she pay in all ?

= _____ + _____ + _____ = _____ + _____ + _____ = _____ + _____ = ☐

❑ There were 426 cookies in a platter. 45 more cookies were placed in it. How many cookies had the platter in all ?

= _____ + _____ + _____ = _____ + _____ + _____ = _____ + _____ = ☐

❑ There are 810 trees in a garden. The gardener plants 38 more trees in it. How many trees has the garden in all now ?

= _____ + _____ + _____ = _____ + _____ + _____ = _____ + _____ = ☐

❑ A florist has 143 rose flowers in his shop. He buys 69 marigold flowers as well. How many flowers are in there in the shop in all ?

= _____ + _____ + _____ = _____ + _____ + _____ = _____ + _____ = ☐

❑ A factory had 785 workers. 19 more workers were employed in it. How many workers had the factory in all ?

= _____ + _____ + _____ = _____ + _____ + _____ = _____ + _____ = ☐

❑ There were 503 mangoes in a big basket. 58 more mangoes were placed in it. How many mangoes had the basket in all ?

= _____ + _____ + _____ = _____ + _____ + _____ = _____ + _____ = ☐

❑ A marriage-party had 847 guests. 40 more guests join the party. How many guests had it in all ?

= _____ + _____ + _____ = _____ + _____ + _____ = _____ + _____ = ☐

8 ADDING 2-DIGIT AND 3-DIGIT NUMERALS—II

READ CAREFULLY

- Break up the 3-digit numeral into **hundreds**, tens and **ones**.
- Break-up the 2-digit numeral also into tens and ones.
- Add up the hundreds, tens and ones to get the total.

$724 + 27$
$= 700 + 20 + 4 + 20 + 7$
$= 700 + 40 + 10 + 1$
$= 700 + 50 + 1 = 751$

$724 + 27 = 751$

DO YOURSELF

A. Do these sums by break-up method :

❑ 456 + 27
= 400 + 50 + 6 + 20 + 7 = 400 + 70 + 13 = ⬚483

❑ 616 + 8

= ____ + ____ + ____ + ____ + ____ = ____ + ____ + ____ = ⬚

❑ 815 + 19

= ____ + ____ + ____ + ____ + ____ = ____ + ____ + ____ = ⬚

❑ 257 + 18

= ____ + ____ + ____ + ____ + ____ = ____ + ____ + ____ = ⬚

❑ 166 + 29

= ____ + ____ + ____ + ____ + ____ = ____ + ____ + ____ = ⬚

❑ 973 + 26

= ____ + ____ + ____ + ____ + ____ = ____ + ____ + ____ = ⬚

❑ 546 + 38

= ____ + ____ + ____ + ____ + ____ = ____ + ____ + ____ = ⬚

B. Solve the following problems mentally :

❑ A school has 451 students. 28 more students are admitted in that school. How many students has the school got in all ?

= _____ + _____ + _____ + _____ + _____ = _____ + _____ + _____ = ☐

❑ A baker bakes 161 cookies for a customer. He has to bake 35 more cookies. How many cookies does he bake in all ?

= _____ + _____ + _____ + _____ + _____ = _____ + _____ + _____ = ☐

❑ A cart has 528 watermelons loaded on it. 24 more watermelons are placed on it. How many watermelons has the cart got in all ?

= _____ + _____ + _____ + _____ + _____ = _____ + _____ + _____ = ☐

❑ A fruit-seller bought 906 mangoes from the market. He had to buy 68 more mangoes for his customers. How many mangoes did he buy in all ?

= _____ + _____ + _____ + _____ + _____ = _____ + _____ + _____ = ☐

❑ A writer writes 345 pages of a book in a month. He writes 25 more pages to complete it. How many pages does he write in all ?

= _____ + _____ + _____ + _____ + _____ = _____ + _____ + _____ = ☐

❑ There are 584 guests in a marriage-party. 16 more guests arrive to take part in it. What is the total number of guests in the party ?

= _____ + _____ + _____ + _____ + _____ = _____ + _____ + _____ = ☐

❑ Bess bought a fur-coat for $ 452. She had to pay $ 45 as tax on it. How much did she pay in all ?

= _____ + _____ + _____ + _____ + _____ = _____ + _____ + _____ = ☐

❑ There are 824 employees in a factory. 65 more people are employed in it. What is the total number of employees in the factory ?

= _____ + _____ + _____ + _____ + _____ = _____ + _____ + _____ = ☐

❑ A baker buys 635 eggs from a farmer. His own hens lay 57 more eggs. How many eggs has the baker got in all ?

= _____ + _____ + _____ + _____ + _____ = _____ + _____ + _____ = ☐

❑ A basket has 247 mangoes. 75 more mangoes are placed in it. How many mangoes has the basket got in all ?

= _____ + _____ + _____ + _____ + _____ = _____ + _____ + _____ = ☐

⑨ ADDING 2-DIGIT AND 3-DIGIT NUMERALS—III

READ CAREFULLY

- Break up the 3-digit numeral into **hundreds**, **tens** and **ones**.

- Round up the 2-digit numeral to the nearest ten.

- Add up the hundreds, tens and ones to get the total.

$547 + 39$
$= 500 + 40 + 7 + 40 - 1$
$= 500 + 80 + 7 - 1$
$= 580 + 6 = 586$

$547 + 39 = 86$

DO YOURSELF

A. Do these sums by break-up method :

❑ $237 + 48$
$= 200 + 30 + 7 + 50 - 2 = 280 + 7 - 2 = 280 + 5 = \boxed{285}$

❑ $863 + 28$

= ___ + ___ + ___ + ___ − ___ = ___ + ___ − ___ = ___ + ___ = ☐

❑ $545 + 39$

= ___ + ___ + ___ + ___ − ___ = ___ + ___ − ___ = ___ + ___ = ☐

❑ $135 + 68$

= ___ + ___ + ___ + ___ − ___ = ___ + ___ − ___ = ___ + ___ = ☐

❑ $428 + 65$

= ___ + ___ + ___ + ___ − ___ = ___ + ___ − ___ = ___ + ___ = ☐

❑ $354 + 39$

= ___ + ___ + ___ + ___ − ___ = ___ + ___ − ___ = ___ + ___ = ☐

❑ $907 + 29$

= ___ + ___ + ___ + ___ − ___ = ___ + ___ − ___ = ___ + ___ = ☐

B. Solve the following problems mentally :

❑ Kate bought a blazer for $ 276. She had to pay $ 27 as surcharge also. How much had she to pay in all ?

= ___ + ___ + ___ + ___ − ___ = ___ + ___ − ___ = ___ + ___ = ☐

❑ A factory has 729 workers. 57 more workers were employed in it. How many workers has the factory got now ?

= ___ + ___ + ___ + ___ − ___ = ___ + ___ − ___ = ___ + ___ = ☐

❑ A cart has 824 pumpkins loaded on it. 47 more pumpkins are placed on it. How many pumpkins has the cart got in all ?

= ___ + ___ + ___ + ___ − ___ = ___ + ___ − ___ = ___ + ___ = ☐

❑ There are 916 students in a school. 19 more students get admission in that school. Find the total number of students.

= ___ + ___ + ___ + ___ − ___ = ___ + ___ − ___ = ___ + ___ = ☐

❑ A baker buys 341 eggs from a farmer. His own hens lay 17 more eggs. How many eggs has the baker got in all ?

= ___ + ___ + ___ + ___ − ___ = ___ + ___ − ___ = ___ + ___ = ☐

❑ A man reads 133 pages of a book during the day. He reads 59 more pages at night. Find the total number of pages read by him.

= ___ + ___ + ___ + ___ − ___ = ___ + ___ − ___ = ___ + ___ = ☐

❑ There are 729 soldiers in a fort. 67 more soldiers are sent there. Find the total number of soldiers in the fort.

= ___ + ___ + ___ + ___ − ___ = ___ + ___ − ___ = ___ + ___ = ☐

❑ A basket has 367 mangoes in it. 28 more mangoes are placed in it. Find the total number of mangoes in the basket.

= ___ + ___ + ___ + ___ − ___ = ___ + ___ − ___ = ___ + ___ = ☐

❑ A baker bakes 856 cookies in the first lot. He has to bake 36 more cookies for his customers. How many cookies does he bake in all ?

= ___ + ___ + ___ + ___ − ___ = ___ + ___ − ___ = ___ + ___ = ☐

❑ There are 553 chocolates in a platter. 48 more chocolates are placed in it. Find the total number of chocolates in the platter.

= ___ + ___ + ___ + ___ − ___ = ___ + ___ − ___ = ___ + ___ = ☐

READ CAREFULLY

- Break up one number into **hundreds**, **tens** and **ones**.

- Break up the other numeral in the same way.

- Add up the hundreds, tens and ones to get the total.

$$326 + 113$$
$$= 300 + 20 + 6 + 100 + 10 + 3$$
$$= 400 + 30 + 9 = 439$$

$$326 + 113 = 439$$

DO YOURSELF

A. Do these sums by break-up method :

❑ 274 + 425
= 200 + 70 + 4 + 400 + 20 + 5 = 600 + 90 + 9 = 699

❑ 573 + 316
= ___ + ___ + ___ + ___ + ___ + ___ = ___ + ___ + ___ =

❑ 613 + 144
= ___ + ___ + ___ + ___ + ___ + ___ = ___ + ___ + ___ =

❑ 815 + 132
= ___ + ___ + ___ + ___ + ___ + ___ = ___ + ___ + ___ =

❑ 526 + 163
= ___ + ___ + ___ + ___ + ___ + ___ = ___ + ___ + ___ =

❑ 482 + 516
= ___ + ___ + ___ + ___ + ___ + ___ = ___ + ___ + ___ =

❑ 373 + 225
= ___ + ___ + ___ + ___ + ___ + ___ = ___ + ___ + ___ =

B. Solve the following problems mentally :

- Mrs Brown buys 418 strawberries at first and 321 strawberries later on. How many strawberries does she buy in all ?

  = ___ + ___ + ___ + ___ + ___ + ___ = ___ + ___ + ___ = ☐

- Andrews writes 236 pages of a book in one month and 222 pages in the next month to complete the book. How many pages does he write in all ?

  = ___ + ___ + ___ + ___ + ___ + ___ = ___ + ___ + ___ = ☐

- There were 375 eggs with a baker. He buys 534 eggs more for his customers. How many eggs does he sell in all ?

  = ___ + ___ + ___ + ___ + ___ + ___ = ___ + ___ + ___ = ☐

- A fruit-seller has 855 oranges in his shop. He buys 114 more oranges. How many oranges are there in his shop in all ?

  = ___ + ___ + ___ + ___ + ___ + ___ = ___ + ___ + ___ = ☐

- Mary buys a dress for $ 234 and another dress for $ 215. How much money does Mary spend in all ?

  = ___ + ___ + ___ + ___ + ___ + ___ = ___ + ___ + ___ = ☐

- There are 467 men in a factory. 371 more men are employed in it. Find the total number of workers in the factory.

  = ___ + ___ + ___ + ___ + ___ + ___ = ___ + ___ + ___ = ☐

- A fort has 774 soldiers in it. 173 more soldiers are sent to that fort. Find the total number of soldiers in the fort.

  = ___ + ___ + ___ + ___ + ___ + ___ = ___ + ___ + ___ = ☐

- A marriage-party has 522 guests. 136 more guests arrive to take part in it. Find the total number of guests.

  = ___ + ___ + ___ + ___ + ___ + ___ = ___ + ___ + ___ = ☐

- 624 pilgrims set out to visit a shrine. 215 more pilgrims join them on the way. Find the total number of pilgrims.

  = ___ + ___ + ___ + ___ + ___ + ___ = ___ + ___ + ___ = ☐

- A school has 555 students on its roll on April 1. 372 more students are admitted in this school for the new year. Find the total number of students.

  = ___ + ___ + ___ + ___ + ___ + ___ = ___ + ___ + ___ = ☐

⑪ ADDITION OF 3-DIGIT NUMERALS—II

- Break up one of the numerals to make the other numeral with complete tens.

- Then add hundreds, tens and ones to get the total.

$$238 + 222$$
$$= 238 + 2 + 220$$
$$= 240 + 220 = 660$$
$$238 + 222 = 660$$

DO YOURSELF

A. Do these sums by break-up method :

❑ 366 + 174

$$= 366 + 4 + 170 = 370 + 100 + 30 + 40 = 400 + 100 + 40 = \boxed{540}$$

❑ 817 + 133

= ___ + ___ + ___ = ___ + ___ + ___ + ___ = ___ + ___ + ___ = ☐

❑ 506 + 184

= ___ + ___ + ___ = ___ + ___ + ___ + ___ = ___ + ___ + ___ = ☐

❑ 446 + 344

= ___ + ___ + ___ = ___ + ___ + ___ + ___ = ___ + ___ + ___ = ☐

❑ 511 + 219

= ___ + ___ + ___ = ___ + ___ + ___ + ___ = ___ + ___ + ___ = ☐

❑ 383 + 217

= ___ + ___ + ___ = ___ + ___ + ___ + ___ = ___ + ___ + ___ = ☐

❑ 672 + 228

= ___ + ___ + ___ = ___ + ___ + ___ + ___ = ___ + ___ + ___ = ☐

❑ 776 + 154

= ___ + ___ + ___ = ___ + ___ + ___ + ___ = ___ + ___ + ___ = ☐

B. Solve the following problems mentally :

☐ There are 426 trees in a garden. 114 more trees are planted in it. Find the total number of trees in the garden.

= ___ + ___ + ___ = ___ + ___ + ___ + ___ = ___ + ___ + ___ = ☐

☐ A man reads 183 pages of a book on Monday. He reads 517 pages in the next two days. How many pages does he read in all ?

= ___ + ___ + ___ = ___ + ___ + ___ + ___ = ___ + ___ + ___ = ☐

☐ There are 817 sheep in a flock. 133 more sheep are bought by the owner of the flock. Find the total number of sheep in the flock.

= ___ + ___ + ___ = ___ + ___ + ___ + ___ = ___ + ___ + ___ = ☐

☐ There are 456 workers in a factory. 324 more workers are employed to complete a contract in time. Find the total number of workers in the factory.

= ___ + ___ + ___ = ___ + ___ + ___ + ___ = ___ + ___ + ___ = ☐

☐ 482 watermelons were loaded on a cart. 508 more watermelons are placed on it. Find the total number of watermelons on the cart.

= ___ + ___ + ___ = ___ + ___ + ___ + ___ = ___ + ___ + ___ = ☐

☐ 373 pilgrims leave for a shrine from a camp. 217 more pilgrims join them on the way. Find the total number of pilgrims.

= ___ + ___ + ___ = ___ + ___ + ___ + ___ = ___ + ___ + ___ = ☐

☐ A school has 521 students on April 1. 309 more students are admitted for the new year. Find the total number of students.

= ___ + ___ + ___ = ___ + ___ + ___ + ___ = ___ + ___ + ___ = ☐

☐ A regiment has 728 soldiers. 132 more soldiers are sent to join this regiment. Find the total number of soldiers in the regiment.

= ___ + ___ + ___ = ___ + ___ + ___ + ___ = ___ + ___ + ___ = ☐

☐ A mill has 756 workers. 144 more workers are employed to complete a contract on time. Find the total number of workers.

= ___ + ___ + ___ = ___ + ___ + ___ + ___ = ___ + ___ + ___ = ☐

☐ There are 856 cows in a herd. The owner of the herd buys 124 more cows. Find the total number of cows in the herd.

= ___ + ___ + ___ = ___ + ___ + ___ + ___ = ___ + ___ + ___ = ☐

12 ADDITION OF 3-DIGIT NUMERALS—III

- Round off the numerals to the nearest hundred.

- Then add the 3-digit numerals and take away the digit from the sum to get the total.

$$346 + 299$$
$$= 346 + 300 - 1$$
$$= 646 - 1 = 645$$
$$346 + 299 = 645$$

DO YOURSELF

A. Do these sums by break-up method :

▢ 184 + 397

= 184 + 400 − 3 = 584 − 3 = $\boxed{581}$

▢ 585 + 398

= _____ + _____ − _____ = _____ − _____ = $\boxed{}$

▢ 754 + 199

= _____ + _____ − _____ = _____ − _____ = $\boxed{}$

▢ 486 + 497

= _____ + _____ − _____ = _____ − _____ = $\boxed{}$

▢ 239 + 495

= _____ + _____ − _____ = _____ − _____ = $\boxed{}$

▢ 519 + 198

= _____ + _____ − _____ = _____ − _____ = $\boxed{}$

▢ 767 + 196

= _____ + _____ − _____ = _____ − _____ = $\boxed{}$

▢ 509 + 396

= _____ + _____ − _____ = _____ − _____ = $\boxed{}$

B. Solve the following problems mentally :

❑ There are 539 sheep in a flock. The owner buys 288 more sheep. How many sheep are there in all in the flock ?

= _____ + _____ – _____ = _____ – _____ = [   ]

❑ 359 pumpkins were loaded on a cart. Later on 397 more pumpkins were placed on it. Find the total number of pumpkins on the cart.

= _____ + _____ – _____ = _____ – _____ = [   ]

❑ There were 589 soldiers in a fort. 427 more soldiers were sent there. Find the total number of soldiers in the fort.

= _____ + _____ – _____ = _____ – _____ = [   ]

❑ There are 499 workers in a mill. 308 more workers were employed to complete a contract in time. Find the total number of workers in the mill.

= _____ + _____ – _____ = _____ – _____ = [   ]

❑ 639 tourists set out to visit a shrine. 287 tourists joined them on the way. Find the total number of tourists.

= _____ + _____ – _____ = _____ – _____ = [   ]

❑ There were 457 trees in a garden. 285 more trees were planted in the garden. Find the total number of trees in the garden.

= _____ + _____ – _____ = _____ – _____ = [   ]

❑ A school has 521 students on April 1. 392 more students are admitted for the new year. Find the total number of students.

= _____ + _____ – _____ = _____ – _____ = [   ]

❑ A platter has 663 cookies in it. 289 more cookies are placed in it. Find the total number of cookies in the platter.

= _____ + _____ – _____ = _____ – _____ = [   ]

❑ 395 labourers were employed to dig a canal. 196 more labourers had to be employed to dig the canal in time. Find the total number of labourers at work.

= _____ + _____ – _____ = _____ – _____ = [   ]

❑ A cowherd has 675 cows. He buys 296 more cows. Find the total number of cows with the cowherd.

= _____ + _____ – _____ = _____ – _____ = [   ]

13 SUBTRACTING ONES FROM 3-DIGIT NUMERALS—I

READ CAREFULLY

- Break up the 3-digit numeral into **hundreds**, **tens** and **ones**.
- Subtract the **ones from ones**.
- Write the remaining numeral as **remainder**.

$$385 - 2$$
$$= 300 + 80 + 5 - 2$$
$$= 300 + 80 + 3 = 383$$

$$385 - 2 = 383$$

DO YOURSELF

A. Do these sums by break-up method :

❑ 347 − 4

300 + 40 + 7 − 4 = 300 + 40 + 3 = $\boxed{343}$

❑ 565 − 2

____ + ____ + ___ − ____ = ____ + ____ + ____ =

❑ 938 − 5

____ + ____ + ___ − ____ = ____ + ____ + ____ =

❑ 438 − 6

____ + ____ + ___ − ____ = ____ + ____ + ____ =

❑ 548 − 4

____ + ____ + ___ − ____ = ____ + ____ + ____ =

❑ 757 − 6

____ + ____ + ___ − ____ = ____ + ____ + ____ =

❑ 659 − 7

____ + ____ + ___ − ____ = ____ + ____ + ____ =

B. Solve these sums mentally :

❏ 448 – 4

_____ + _____ + ___ – _____ = _____ + _____ + _____ = [ ]

❏ 926 – 3

_____ + _____ + ___ – _____ = _____ + _____ + _____ = [ ]

❏ 697 – 5

_____ + _____ + ___ – _____ = _____ + _____ + _____ = [ ]

❏ 758 – 6

_____ + _____ + ___ – _____ = _____ + _____ + _____ = [ ]

❏ 689 – 7

_____ + _____ + ___ – _____ = _____ + _____ + _____ = [ ]

❏ 546 – 3

_____ + _____ + ___ – _____ = _____ + _____ + _____ = [ ]

❏ 238 – 2

_____ + _____ + ___ – _____ = _____ + _____ + _____ = [ ]

❏ 399 – 8

_____ + _____ + ___ – _____ = _____ + _____ + _____ = [ ]

❏ 699 – 1

_____ + _____ + ___ – _____ = _____ + _____ + _____ = [ ]

❏ 847 – 5

_____ + _____ + ___ – _____ = _____ + _____ + _____ = [ ]

❏ 698 – 7

_____ + _____ + ___ – _____ = _____ + _____ + _____ = [ ]

C. Solve the following problems **mentally** :

- Mr Robert bought 647 eggs. He gave away 5 eggs to beggars. How many eggs were left with him ?

  _____ + ____ + ___ – ____ = _____ + ____ + ____ = [   ]

- There were 729 guests in a party. 7 of them left. How many guests were there in the party then ?

  _____ + ____ + ___ – ____ = _____ + ____ + ____ = [   ]

- A baker bakes 528 biscuits. He gives away 9 biscuits to children. How many biscuits has he got now ?

  _____ + ____ + ___ – ____ = _____ + ____ + ____ = [   ]

- Ann bought a dress for $ 656. She was given $ 5 as discount. How much did she pay for the dress ?

  _____ + ____ + ___ – ____ = _____ + ____ + ____ = [   ]

- Ronald writes 227 pages of a book in a week. 6 of the pages were spoiled. How many pages were left intact ?

  _____ + ____ + ___ – ____ = _____ + ____ + ____ = [   ]

- A baker bakes 489 cookies for his customers. He gives away 5 cookies to beggars. How many cookies are left with him ?

  _____ + ____ + ___ – ____ = _____ + ____ + ____ = [   ]

- A cart had 846 pumpkins loaded on it. 4 pumpkins roll off the cart. How many pumpkins were left on the cart ?

  _____ + ____ + ___ – ____ = _____ + ____ + ____ = [   ]

- A school has 628 students on roll. 6 of them leave the school. How many students has the school got now ?

  _____ + ____ + ___ – ____ = _____ + ____ + ____ = [   ]

- A labourer earns $ 165 daily. He gives away $ 4 in a church as donation. What is his net daily income ?

  _____ + ____ + ___ – ____ = _____ + ____ + ____ = [   ]

- A marriage-party has 384 guests. 3 guests leave the party. How many guests are left behind ?

  _____ + ____ + ___ – ____ = _____ + ____ + ____ = [   ]

14 SUBTRACTING ONES FROM 3-DIGIT NUMERALS—II

- Break up the 3-digit numerals such that a **ten** gets separate from it.

- Then subtract the digit from the **ten** to get the remainder.

$$275 - 7$$
$$= 265 + 10 - 7$$
$$= 265 + 3 = 268$$
$$275 - 7 = 268$$

DO YOURSELF

A. Do these sums by break-up method :

□ $342 - 4$

$= 332 + 10 - 4 = 332 + 6 = \boxed{338}$

□ $733 - 6$

$= \underline{\hspace{2cm}} + \underline{\hspace{2cm}} - \underline{\hspace{2cm}} = \underline{\hspace{2cm}} + \underline{\hspace{2cm}} = \boxed{}$

□ $416 - 8$

$= \underline{\hspace{2cm}} + \underline{\hspace{2cm}} - \underline{\hspace{2cm}} = \underline{\hspace{2cm}} + \underline{\hspace{2cm}} = \boxed{}$

□ $565 - 7$

$= \underline{\hspace{2cm}} + \underline{\hspace{2cm}} - \underline{\hspace{2cm}} = \underline{\hspace{2cm}} + \underline{\hspace{2cm}} = \boxed{}$

□ $631 - 5$

$= \underline{\hspace{2cm}} + \underline{\hspace{2cm}} - \underline{\hspace{2cm}} = \underline{\hspace{2cm}} + \underline{\hspace{2cm}} = \boxed{}$

□ $832 - 9$

$= \underline{\hspace{2cm}} + \underline{\hspace{2cm}} - \underline{\hspace{2cm}} = \underline{\hspace{2cm}} + \underline{\hspace{2cm}} = \boxed{}$

□ $470 - 2$

$= \underline{\hspace{2cm}} + \underline{\hspace{2cm}} - \underline{\hspace{2cm}} = \underline{\hspace{2cm}} + \underline{\hspace{2cm}} = \boxed{}$

□ $930 - 1$

$= \underline{\hspace{2cm}} + \underline{\hspace{2cm}} - \underline{\hspace{2cm}} = \underline{\hspace{2cm}} + \underline{\hspace{2cm}} = \boxed{}$

B. Solve the following problems **mentally** :

❑ Tom has 322 marbles. He loses 5 marbles in a game. How many marbles has he got now ?

= _____ + _____ − _____ = _____ + _____ = [_____]

❑ There are 603 soldiers in a fort. 8 soldiers leave the fort. How many soldiers has the fort got now ?

= _____ + _____ − _____ = _____ + _____ = [_____]

❑ A chef bakes 831 biscuits. He gives away 6 biscuits to children. How many biscuits has he got now ?

= _____ + _____ − _____ = _____ + _____ = [_____]

❑ A writer writes 321 pages of a book in a month. 4 pages get lost somewhere How many written pages are left behind ?

= _____ + _____ − _____ = _____ + _____ = [_____]

❑ A florist has 441 rose flowers. He offers 8 flowers in a temple. How many flowers are left with him now ?

= _____ + _____ − _____ = _____ + _____ = [_____]

❑ There were 902 students in a school. 8 students leave the school. How many students has the school got now ?

= _____ + _____ − _____ = _____ + _____ = [_____]

❑ 571 watermelons were loaded on a camel-cart. 9 watermelons roll off the cart. How many watermelons are there on the cart now ?

= _____ + _____ − _____ = _____ + _____ = [_____]

❑ A basket has 311 mangoes in it. 9 mangoes are sold to customers. How many mangoes are there in the basket now ?

= _____ + _____ − _____ = _____ + _____ = [_____]

❑ There were 822 soldiers in a fort. 8 soldiers fall ill and die. How many soldiers are there in the fort now ?

= _____ + _____ − _____ = _____ + _____ = [_____]

❑ A garden has 512 trees in it. 7 trees are uprooted by a storm. How many trees are there in the garden now ?

= _____ + _____ − _____ = _____ + _____ = [_____]

15 SUBTRACTING ONES FROM 3-DIGIT NUMERALS—III

READ CAREFULLY

- Break up the digit such that its one part is the same as the one's digit in the 3-digit numeral.

- Subtract this part to get 0 in the one's place of the 3-digit numeral.

- Subtract the other part to get the remainder.

$$325 - 8$$
$$= 325 - 5 - 3$$
$$= 320 - 3 = 317$$

$$325 - 8 = 317$$

DO YOURSELF

A. Do these sums by break-up method :

◻ 231 – 2
= 231 – 1 – 1 = 230 – 1 = $\boxed{229}$

◻ 596 – 7

= _____ – _____ – _____ = _____ – _____ = ☐

◻ 293 – 4

= _____ – _____ – _____ = _____ – _____ = ☐

◻ 762 – 8

= _____ – _____ – _____ = _____ – _____ = ☐

◻ 595 – 6

= _____ – _____ – _____ = _____ – _____ = ☐

◻ 414 – 9

= _____ – _____ – _____ = _____ – _____ = ☐

◻ 812 – 5

= _____ – _____ – _____ = _____ – _____ = ☐

◻ 643 – 5

= _____ – _____ – _____ = _____ – _____ = ☐

B. Solve the following problems mentally :

❑ A cap-seller has 123 caps. He sells 8 caps out of them. How many caps has he got now ?

= _____ − _____ − _____ = _____ − _____ = ☐

❑ There are 838 mangoes in a basket. 9 mangoes are sold away. How many mangoes are there in the basket now ?

= _____ − _____ − _____ = _____ − _____ = ☐

❑ There were 327 soldiers in a regiment. 9 soldiers were killed in a battle. How many soldiers were left in the regiment ?

= _____ − _____ − _____ = _____ − _____ = ☐

❑ Bess bought a dress for $ 242. She got a discount of $ 8 on the dress. How much did she pay for it ?

= _____ − _____ − _____ = _____ − _____ = ☐

❑ A cart was loaded with 753 pumpkins. 8 pumpkins rolled off the cart. How many pumpkins were left on the cart now ?

= _____ − _____ − _____ = _____ − _____ = ☐

❑ A baker cooks 992 biscuits. He gives away 9 biscuits to children. How many biscuits are left with him now ?

= _____ − _____ − _____ = _____ − _____ = ☐

❑ A fruit-seller bought 444 oranges. He gave away 7 oranges to beggars. How many oranges were left with him ?

= _____ − _____ − _____ = _____ − _____ = ☐

❑ A factory has 672 workers. 8 workers are dismissed from service. How many workers has the factory got now ?

= _____ − _____ − _____ = _____ − _____ = ☐

❑ A platter has 522 cookies in it. 6 cookies were sold off. How many cookies has the platter got now ?

= _____ − _____ − _____ = _____ − _____ = ☐

❑ There were 552 guests at a marriage-party. 6 of them left. How many guests were left behind ?

= _____ − _____ − _____ = _____ − _____ = ☐

16 SUBTRACTING 2-DIGIT NUMERALS FROM 3-DIGIT NUMERALS—I

- Break up the 3-digit numeral into hundreds, tens and ones.
- Break-up the 2-digit numeral into tens and ones.
- Subtract tens from tens and ones from ones.

$$648 - 24$$
$$= 600 + 40 + 8 - 20 - 4$$
$$= 600 + 20 + 4 = 624$$

$$648 - 24 = 624$$

DO YOURSELF

A. Do these sums by break-up method :

□ 445 – 32
$$= 400 + 40 + 5 - 30 - 2 = 400 + 10 + 3 = \boxed{413}$$

□ 494 – 43
$$= \underline{\quad} + \underline{\quad} + \underline{\quad} - \underline{\quad} - \underline{\quad} = \underline{\quad} + \underline{\quad} + \underline{\quad} = \boxed{}$$

□ 625 – 14
$$= \underline{\quad} + \underline{\quad} + \underline{\quad} - \underline{\quad} - \underline{\quad} = \underline{\quad} + \underline{\quad} + \underline{\quad} = \boxed{}$$

□ 867 – 55
$$= \underline{\quad} + \underline{\quad} + \underline{\quad} - \underline{\quad} - \underline{\quad} = \underline{\quad} + \underline{\quad} + \underline{\quad} = \boxed{}$$

□ 942 – 31
$$= \underline{\quad} + \underline{\quad} + \underline{\quad} - \underline{\quad} - \underline{\quad} = \underline{\quad} + \underline{\quad} + \underline{\quad} = \boxed{}$$

□ 587 – 76
$$= \underline{\quad} + \underline{\quad} + \underline{\quad} - \underline{\quad} - \underline{\quad} = \underline{\quad} + \underline{\quad} + \underline{\quad} = \boxed{}$$

□ 848 – 37
$$= \underline{\quad} + \underline{\quad} + \underline{\quad} - \underline{\quad} - \underline{\quad} = \underline{\quad} + \underline{\quad} + \underline{\quad} = \boxed{}$$

□ 956 – 44
$$= \underline{\quad} + \underline{\quad} + \underline{\quad} - \underline{\quad} - \underline{\quad} = \underline{\quad} + \underline{\quad} + \underline{\quad} = \boxed{}$$

B. Solve the following problems **mentally** :

- A baker bakes 558 biscuits. He sells of 37 biscuits out of them. How many biscuits has he got now ?

    = _____ + _____ + _____ − _____ − _____ = _____ + _____ + _____ = ☐

- A cart is loaded with 729 papayas. 18 papayas roll off the cart. How many papayas are there on the cart now ?

    = _____ + _____ + _____ − _____ − _____ = _____ + _____ + _____ = ☐

- A school has 656 students. 32 students leave the school. How many students are there in the school now ?

    = _____ + _____ + _____ − _____ − _____ = _____ + _____ + _____ = ☐

- Kate buys a dress for $ 165 for Christmas. She gets a discount of $ 23. How much does she pay for the dress ?

    = _____ + _____ + _____ − _____ − _____ = _____ + _____ + _____ = ☐

- There were 489 biscuits in a platter. 45 biscuits were sold off.. How many biscuits were there in the platter now ?

    = _____ + _____ + _____ − _____ − _____ = _____ + _____ + _____ = ☐

- A garden had 847 trees in it. 34 trees get uprooted due to a storm. How many trees has the garden got now ?

    = _____ + _____ + _____ − _____ − _____ = _____ + _____ + _____ = ☐

- A fruit-seller has 274 apples in his shop. He sells 51 apples out of them. How many apples are there in the shop now ?

    = _____ + _____ + _____ − _____ − _____ = _____ + _____ + _____ = ☐

- A factory had 384 workers. 51 workers were shunted out. How many workers were left behind ?

    = _____ + _____ + _____ − _____ − _____ = _____ + _____ + _____ = ☐

- There were 638 soldiers in a fort. 26 soldiers were sent to a hospital. How many soldiers were there in the fort now ?

    = _____ + _____ + _____ − _____ − _____ = _____ + _____ + _____ = ☐

- A marriage-party had 267 guests. 24 guests leave the party. How many guests were left in the marriage-party ?

    = _____ + _____ + _____ − _____ − _____ = _____ + _____ + _____ = ☐

17 SUBTRACTING 2-DIGIT NUMERALS FROM 3-DIGIT NUMERALS—II

- Break up the 3-digit numeral such that its one part is the next higher ten than the 2-digit numeral.

- Subtract the 2-digit numeral from the ten and add the remainder to the other part of the 3-digit numeral.

$$744 - 38$$
$$= 704 + 40 - 38$$
$$= 704 + 2 = 706$$
$$744 - 38 = 706$$

DO YOURSELF

A. Do these sums by break-up method :

◻ 472 – 35
   = 432 + 40 – 35 = 432 + 5 = $\boxed{437}$

◻ 432 – 26

   = _____ + _____ – _____ = _____ + _____ = ☐

◻ 569 – 17

   = _____ + _____ – _____ = _____ + _____ = ☐

◻ 632 – 14

   = _____ + _____ – _____ = _____ + _____ = ☐

◻ 281 – 38

   = _____ + _____ – _____ = _____ + _____ = ☐

◻ 554 – 46

   = _____ + _____ – _____ = _____ + _____ = ☐

◻ 895 – 77

   = _____ + _____ – _____ = _____ + _____ = ☐

B. Solve the following problems mentally :

☐ A school has 973 students. 52 students leave the school. How many students has the school got now ?

= _____ + _____ − _____ = _____ + _____ = ☐

☐ A chef bakes 654 cookies. He sells 34 cookies to customers. How many cookies has the chef got now ?

= _____ + _____ − _____ = _____ + _____ = ☐

☐ A basket has 596 mangoes in it. 83 mangoes are sold away. How many mangoes has the basket got now ?

= _____ + _____ − _____ = _____ + _____ = ☐

☐ A fruit-seller bought 938 oranges from the market. He sold away 26 oranges at once. How many oranges has he got now ?

= _____ + _____ − _____ = _____ + _____ = ☐

☐ A writer writes 187 pages of a book in a week. 54 pages written by him get lost. How many pages are left with him ?

= _____ + _____ − _____ = _____ + _____ = ☐

☐ There were 887 soldiers in a fort. 54 soldiers were killed in a battle. How many soldiers were left behind in the fort ?

= _____ + _____ − _____ = _____ + _____ = ☐

☐ Lucy buys a fur-coat for $ 152. She gets a discount of $ 13. How much does she pay for the coat ?

= _____ + _____ − _____ = _____ + _____ = ☐

☐ There are 658 employees in a mill. 37 of them are dismissed from service. How many employees has the mill got now ?

= _____ + _____ − _____ = _____ + _____ = ☐

☐ A baker has 268 eggs. 48 eggs go bad. How many good eggs are left with the baker ?

= _____ + _____ − _____ = _____ + _____ = ☐

☐ A cart had 731 melons loaded on it. 25 melons rolled off the cart. How many melons were left in the cart ?

= _____ + _____ − _____ = _____ + _____ = ☐

18 SUBTRACTING 2-DIGIT NUMERALS FROM 3-DIGIT NUMERALS—III

READ CAREFULLY

- Break up the 2-digit numeral such that its one part has the same one's digit as the 3-digit numeral has.
- Subtract this part from the 3-digit numeral.
- Then subtract the other part.

$244 - 29$
$= 244 - 24 - 5$
$= 220 - 5 = 215$
$244 - 29 = 215$

DO YOURSELF

A. Do these sums by break-up method :

❑ 366 – 38
= 366 – 36 – 2 = 330 – 2 = $\boxed{328}$

❑ 862 – 46

= _____ – _____ – _____ = _____ – _____ = ☐

❑ 354 – 26

= _____ – _____ – _____ = _____ – _____ = ☐

❑ 594 – 66

= _____ – _____ – _____ = _____ – _____ = ☐

❑ 687 – 49

= _____ – _____ – _____ = _____ – _____ = ☐

❑ 485 – 58

= _____ – _____ – _____ = _____ – _____ = ☐

❑ 245 – 28

= _____ – _____ – _____ = _____ – _____ = ☐

B. Solve the following problems **mentally** :

- Tom bought a blazer for $ 170. He got $ 29 as discount. How much had he to pay for the blazer ?

  = _____ − _____ − _____ = _____ − _____ = ☐

- A factory has 983 workers. 47 workers are dismissed by the manager. How many workers were left in the factory ?

  = _____ − _____ − _____ = _____ − _____ = ☐

- A cart has 756 papayas loaded on it. 39 papayas roll off the cart. How many papayas has the cart got now ?

  = _____ − _____ − _____ = _____ − _____ = ☐

- There were 893 students in a school. 49 students left the school. How many students were left in the school ?

  = _____ − _____ − _____ = _____ − _____ = ☐

- A baker buys 304 eggs from a farmer. 19 eggs go bad. How many good eggs has the baker got now ?

  = _____ − _____ − _____ = _____ − _____ = ☐

- A person writes 152 pages of a book in a month. 29 pages get lost. How many written pages are left behind ?

  = _____ − _____ − _____ = _____ − _____ = ☐

- A fort had 764 soldiers in it. 38 soldiers get injured and are sent to a hospital. How many soldiers had the fort got now ?

  = _____ − _____ − _____ = _____ − _____ = ☐

- A fruit-seller buys 962 apples from the market. 39 apples are at once sold off. How many apples are left behind ?

  = _____ − _____ − _____ = _____ − _____ = ☐

- A baker bakes 453 cookies. He sells 29 cookies out of them. How many cookies are left behind ?

  = _____ − _____ − _____ = _____ − _____ = ☐

- A platter has 663 chocolates. 49 chocolates are distributed among children. How many chocolates are there in the platter now ?

  = _____ − _____ − _____ = _____ − _____ = ☐

19 SUBTRACTION OF 3-DIGIT NUMERALS—I

READ CAREFULLY

- Break up both the numerals into **hundreds**, **tens** and **ones**.

- Subtract hundreds, tens and ones from hundreds, tens and ones.

$568 - 327$
$= 500 + 60 + 8 - 300 - 20 - 7$
$= 200 + 40 + 1 = 241$

$568 - 327 = 241$

DO YOURSELF

A. Do these sums by break-up method :

❑ 296 – 185
$= 200 + 90 + 6 - 100 - 80 - 5 = 100 + 10 + 1 = \boxed{111}$

❑ 357 – 214
= ___ + ___ + ___ – ___ – ___ – ___ = ___ + ___ + ___ = ☐

❑ 649 – 243
= ___ + ___ + ___ – ___ – ___ – ___ = ___ + ___ + ___ = ☐

❑ 345 – 133
= ___ + ___ + ___ – ___ – ___ – ___ = ___ + ___ + ___ = ☐

❑ 196 – 142
= ___ + ___ + ___ – ___ – ___ – ___ = ___ + ___ + ___ = ☐

❑ 847 – 633
= ___ + ___ + ___ – ___ – ___ – ___ = ___ + ___ + ___ = ☐

❑ 768 – 355
= ___ + ___ + ___ – ___ – ___ – ___ = ___ + ___ + ___ = ☐

B. Solve the following problems **mentally** :

▫ Mr Brownie buys 487 apricots and immediately sells 355 apricots out of them. How many apricots are left behind ?

= ___ + ___ + ___ – ___ – ___ – ___ = ___ + ___ + ___ = ☐

▫ Robert writes 189 pages of a book in a month. 59 pages get lost out of them. How many pages are left with Robert ?

= ___ + ___ + ___ – ___ – ___ – ___ = ___ + ___ + ___ = ☐

▫ There were 266 eggs with a baker. He sold away 153 eggs out of them. How many eggs were left behind ?

= ___ + ___ + ___ – ___ – ___ – ___ = ___ + ___ + ___ = ☐

▫ A fruit-seller has 779 apples in his shop. He sells 537 apples to another shopkeeper. How many apples are left with him ?

= ___ + ___ + ___ – ___ – ___ – ___ = ___ + ___ + ___ = ☐

▫ Kate buys a dress for $ 181 and gets a discount of $ 37. How much has she to pay for the dress ?

= ___ + ___ + ___ – ___ – ___ – ___ = ___ + ___ + ___ = ☐

▫ There are 874 trees in a garden. 371 trees get uprooted due to a storm. How many trees has the garden got now ?

= ___ + ___ + ___ – ___ – ___ – ___ = ___ + ___ + ___ = ☐

▫ A fort has 484 soldiers in it. 278 soldiers are sent to another fort. How many soldiers are left behind ?

= ___ + ___ + ___ – ___ – ___ – ___ = ___ + ___ + ___ = ☐

▫ A birthday party has 765 guests. 232 guests leave the party. How many guests are left behind ?

= ___ + ___ + ___ – ___ – ___ – ___ = ___ + ___ + ___ = ☐

▫ 948 pilgrims set out to visit a shrine. 337 pilgrims fall ill. How many healthy pilgrims go ahead to the shrine ?

= ___ + ___ + ___ – ___ – ___ – ___ = ___ + ___ + ___ = ☐

▫ A school has 941 students on its roll on April 1. 137 students leave the school How many students has the school got now ?

= ___ + ___ + ___ – ___ – ___ – ___ = ___ + ___ + ___ = ☐

20 SUBTRACTION OF 3-DIGIT NUMERALS—II

- Break up the bigger numeral such that one part is the next hundred to the other numerals.

- Subtract the other numeral from the hundreds

$$736 - 589$$
$$= 136 + 600 - 589$$
$$= 136 + 11 = 147$$
$$736 - 589 = 147$$

DO YOURSELF

A. Do these sums by break-up method :

- 610 − 436
  = 110 + 500 − 436 = 110 + 64 = $\boxed{174}$

- 509 − 367

  = _____ + _____ − _____ = _____ + _____ = $\boxed{}$

- 222 − 156

  = _____ + _____ − _____ = _____ + _____ = $\boxed{}$

- 834 − 375

  = _____ + _____ − _____ = _____ + _____ = $\boxed{}$

- 621 − 380

  = _____ + _____ − _____ = _____ + _____ = $\boxed{}$

- 716 − 643

  = _____ + _____ − _____ = _____ + _____ = $\boxed{}$

- 448 − 257

  = _____ + _____ − _____ = _____ + _____ = $\boxed{}$

- 574 − 168

  = _____ + _____ − _____ = _____ + _____ = $\boxed{}$

B. Solve the following problems **mentally** :

- There are 876 soldiers in a fort. 542 soldiers are sent to the battle-field. How many soldiers are left behind in the fort ?

  = _____ + _____ – _____ = _____ + _____ = ☐

- There are 935 cows in a herd. 593 cows are taken to a pasture. How many cows are left behind in the herd ?

  = _____ + _____ – _____ = _____ + _____ = ☐

- There are 945 pumpkins loaded on a cart. 635 pumpkins are transferred to another cart. How many pumpkins are left on the first cart ?

  = _____ + _____ – _____ = _____ + _____ = ☐

- There are 648 workers in a factory. 245 workers are dismissed. How many workers has the factory got now ?

  = _____ + _____ – _____ = _____ + _____ = ☐

- There are 266 cakes in a platter. 154 cakes are distributed among the poor. How many cakes are there in the platter now ?

  = _____ + _____ – _____ = _____ + _____ = ☐

- 778 pilgrims are on the way to a shrine. 538 pilgrims fall ill and are sent to a hospital. Find the number of the remaining pilgrims.

  = _____ + _____ – _____ = _____ + _____ = ☐

- A school has 873 students. 431 students are in the primary section. How many students are there in the upper classes ?

  = _____ + _____ – _____ = _____ + _____ = ☐

- There are 296 trees in an orchard. 132 of them are still small plants. Find the number of the grown-up trees.

  = _____ + _____ – _____ = _____ + _____ = ☐

- There were 266 guests in a marriage-party. 154 of them were females. Find the number of males in the party.

  = _____ + _____ – _____ = _____ + _____ = ☐

- There were 356 mangoes in a basket. 213 mangoes were sold off. Find the number of the remaining mangoes.

  = _____ + _____ – _____ = _____ + _____ = ☐

21 SUBTRACTION OF 3-DIGIT NUMERALS—III

- Break up the smaller numeral such that its one's unit is the same as that of the other numeral.

- Then carry on the subtraction.

$$367 - 229$$
$$= 367 - 227 - 2$$
$$= 140 - 2 = 138$$
$$367 - 227 = 138$$

DO YOURSELF

A. Do these sums by break-up method :

- 986 – 438
  = 986 – 436 – 2 = 550 – 2 = $\boxed{548}$

- 864 – 427

  = _____ – _____ – _____ = _____ – _____ = ☐

- 466 – 229

  = _____ + _____ – _____ = _____ – _____ = ☐

- 646 – 337

  = _____ + _____ – _____ = _____ – _____ = ☐

- 853 – 617

  = _____ + _____ – _____ = _____ – _____ = ☐

- 248 – 119

  = _____ + _____ – _____ = _____ – _____ = ☐

- 546 – 248

  = _____ + _____ – _____ = _____ – _____ = ☐

- 762 – 558

  = _____ + _____ – _____ = _____ – _____ = ☐

B. Solve the following problems **mentally** :

❑ There are 736 sheep in a flock. The owner sells off 588 sheep. How many sheep are left in the flock ?

= _____ + _____ – _____ = _____ – _____ = ☐

❑ 334 watermelons were loaded on a cart. 175 watermelons were sold away. How many watermelons were left on the cart ?

= _____ + _____ – _____ = _____ – _____ = ☐

❑ There were 575 soldiers in a fort. 168 of them were sent to the battle-field. How many soldiers were left in the fort ?

= _____ + _____ – _____ = _____ – _____ = ☐

❑ There are 442 workers in a mill. 258 of them were sent to the other branch of the mill. How many workers are left in the first mill ?

= _____ + _____ – _____ = _____ – _____ = ☐

❑ 521 pilgrims are on the way to a shrine. 388 of them are on foot while others are on horses. Find the number of horse-riders.

= _____ + _____ – _____ = _____ – _____ = ☐

❑ 248 cows were owned by a cowherd. He sold off 109 of them. How many cows were left with him ?

= _____ + _____ – _____ = _____ – _____ = ☐

❑ A school has 472 students. 128 of them are in the senior classes. How many students are in junior classes ?

= _____ + _____ – _____ = _____ – _____ = ☐

❑ There were 674 sheep in a flock. 217 sheep were sent to a pasture. How many sheep were left behind ?

= _____ + _____ – _____ = _____ – _____ = ☐

❑ 952 labourers were employed to dig a canal. 538 labourers went on a strike Find the number of the remaining labourers.

= _____ + _____ – _____ = _____ – _____ = ☐

❑ A basket has 468 mangoes in it. 229 mangoes were sold off to a customer. How many mangoes are left behind ?

= _____ + _____ – _____ = _____ – _____ = ☐

22 ADDING A NUMERAL ENDING IN 9

- Add 10, 20, 30, 40, 50, 60, etc. next to the numeral ending in 9 and add it to the given numeral.

- Subtract 1 from the sum.

$729 + 39$

$= 729 + 40 - 1$

$= 769 - 1 = 768$

$729 + 39 = 768$

DO YOURSELF

A. Do these sums as explained above :

- $8 + 9 \quad = 8 + 10 - 1 = 18 - 1 = \boxed{17}$

- $18 + 19 = \underline{\qquad} + \underline{\qquad} - \underline{\qquad} = \underline{\qquad} - \underline{\qquad} = \boxed{}$

- $16 + 19 = \underline{\qquad} + \underline{\qquad} - \underline{\qquad} = \underline{\qquad} - \underline{\qquad} = \boxed{}$

- $27 + 29 = \underline{\qquad} + \underline{\qquad} - \underline{\qquad} = \underline{\qquad} - \underline{\qquad} = \boxed{}$

- $36 + 39 = \underline{\qquad} + \underline{\qquad} - \underline{\qquad} = \underline{\qquad} - \underline{\qquad} = \boxed{}$

- $22 + 69 = \underline{\qquad} + \underline{\qquad} - \underline{\qquad} = \underline{\qquad} - \underline{\qquad} = \boxed{}$

- $12 + 79 = \underline{\qquad} + \underline{\qquad} - \underline{\qquad} = \underline{\qquad} - \underline{\qquad} = \boxed{}$

- $37 + 49 = \underline{\qquad} + \underline{\qquad} - \underline{\qquad} = \underline{\qquad} - \underline{\qquad} = \boxed{}$

- $43 + 39 = \underline{\qquad} + \underline{\qquad} - \underline{\qquad} = \underline{\qquad} - \underline{\qquad} = \boxed{}$

- $5 + 89 = \underline{\qquad} + \underline{\qquad} - \underline{\qquad} = \underline{\qquad} - \underline{\qquad} = \boxed{}$

- $18 + 69 = \underline{\qquad} + \underline{\qquad} - \underline{\qquad} = \underline{\qquad} - \underline{\qquad} = \boxed{}$

- $36 + 29 = \underline{\qquad} + \underline{\qquad} - \underline{\qquad} = \underline{\qquad} - \underline{\qquad} = \boxed{}$

- $619 + 9 = \underline{\qquad} + \underline{\qquad} - \underline{\qquad} = \underline{\qquad} - \underline{\qquad} = \boxed{}$

- $229 + 19 = \underline{\qquad} + \underline{\qquad} - \underline{\qquad} = \underline{\qquad} - \underline{\qquad} = \boxed{}$

B. Solve the following problems **mentally** :

❑ There are 229 mangoes in a basket. 19 more mangoes were placed in it. How many mangoes has the basket got now ?

= _____ + _____ – _____ = _____ – _____ = ☐

❑ 348 watermelons were loaded on a cart. 29 more watermelons were placed on it. How many watermelons were there in the cart in all?

= _____ + _____ – _____ = _____ – _____ = ☐

❑ There were 445 soldiers in a fort. 39 more soldiers came there. How many soldiers were there in the fort in all ?

= _____ + _____ – _____ = _____ – _____ = ☐

❑ There are 545 workers in a mill. 49 more workers are employed to complete a contract. How many workers are there in the mill in all ?

= _____ + _____ – _____ = _____ – _____ = ☐

❑ 621 pilgrims are on the way to a shrine. 59 more pilgrims join them. Find the total number of pilgrims.

= _____ + _____ – _____ = _____ – _____ = ☐

❑ 712 cows are owned by a cowherd. He buys 69 more cows. How many cows has he got now ?

= _____ + _____ – _____ = _____ – _____ = ☐

❑ A school has 514 students. 79 more students get admission in that school. How many students has the school got in all ?

= _____ + _____ – _____ = _____ – _____ = ☐

❑ There were 304 sheep in a flock. 89 more sheep were brought in. How many sheep has the flock got now ?

= _____ + _____ – _____ = _____ – _____ = ☐

❑ 809 labourers are employed to dig a canal. 9 more labourers have to be employed to finish the work in time. How many labourers are at work ?

= _____ + _____ – _____ = _____ – _____ = ☐

❑ A basket has 858 apples in it. 39 more apples are placed in it. How many apples has the basket got in all ?

= _____ + _____ – _____ = _____ – _____ = ☐

23 SUBTRACTING A NUMERAL ENDING IN 9

- Subtract the nearest next 10 to the smaller numeral from the given numeral.

- Then add 1 to the remainder to get the correct answer.

$152 - 49$

$= 152 - 50 + 1$

$= 102 + 1 = 103$

$152 - 49 = 103$

DO YOURSELF

A. Do these sums as explained above :

$33 - 9 \quad = 33 - 10 + 1 = 23 + 1 = \boxed{24}$

$48 - 19 = \underline{\hspace{1.5cm}} - \underline{\hspace{2cm}} + \underline{\hspace{1cm}} = \underline{\hspace{2cm}} + \underline{\hspace{1cm}} = \boxed{}$

$57 - 29 = \underline{\hspace{1.5cm}} - \underline{\hspace{2cm}} + \underline{\hspace{1cm}} = \underline{\hspace{2cm}} + \underline{\hspace{1cm}} = \boxed{}$

$38 - 9 = \underline{\hspace{1.5cm}} - \underline{\hspace{2cm}} + \underline{\hspace{1cm}} = \underline{\hspace{2cm}} + \underline{\hspace{1cm}} = \boxed{}$

$63 - 39 = \underline{\hspace{1.5cm}} - \underline{\hspace{2cm}} + \underline{\hspace{1cm}} = \underline{\hspace{2cm}} + \underline{\hspace{1cm}} = \boxed{}$

$77 + 49 = \underline{\hspace{1.5cm}} - \underline{\hspace{2cm}} + \underline{\hspace{1cm}} = \underline{\hspace{2cm}} + \underline{\hspace{1cm}} = \boxed{}$

$82 - 59 = \underline{\hspace{1.5cm}} - \underline{\hspace{2cm}} + \underline{\hspace{1cm}} = \underline{\hspace{2cm}} + \underline{\hspace{1cm}} = \boxed{}$

$88 - 69 = \underline{\hspace{1.5cm}} - \underline{\hspace{2cm}} + \underline{\hspace{1cm}} = \underline{\hspace{2cm}} + \underline{\hspace{1cm}} = \boxed{}$

$97 - 79 = \underline{\hspace{1.5cm}} - \underline{\hspace{2cm}} + \underline{\hspace{1cm}} = \underline{\hspace{2cm}} + \underline{\hspace{1cm}} = \boxed{}$

$93 - 39 = \underline{\hspace{1.5cm}} - \underline{\hspace{2cm}} + \underline{\hspace{1cm}} = \underline{\hspace{2cm}} + \underline{\hspace{1cm}} = \boxed{}$

$85 - 49 = \underline{\hspace{1.5cm}} - \underline{\hspace{2cm}} + \underline{\hspace{1cm}} = \underline{\hspace{2cm}} + \underline{\hspace{1cm}} = \boxed{}$

$78 - 29 = \underline{\hspace{1.5cm}} - \underline{\hspace{2cm}} + \underline{\hspace{1cm}} = \underline{\hspace{2cm}} + \underline{\hspace{1cm}} = \boxed{}$

$65 - 19 = \underline{\hspace{1.5cm}} - \underline{\hspace{2cm}} + \underline{\hspace{1cm}} = \underline{\hspace{2cm}} + \underline{\hspace{1cm}} = \boxed{}$

$37 - 9 = \underline{\hspace{1.5cm}} - \underline{\hspace{2cm}} + \underline{\hspace{1cm}} = \underline{\hspace{2cm}} + \underline{\hspace{1cm}} = \boxed{}$

B. Solve the following problems **mentally** :

- There are 436 oranges in a basket. 29 of them are sold off. Find the number of oranges in the basket now.

  = _____ − _____ + _____ = _____ + _____ = [   ]

- 892 pumpkins were loaded on a cart. 89 of them were sold away. How many pumpkins were left in the cart ?

  = _____ − _____ + _____ = _____ + _____ = [   ]

- There were 285 soldiers in a fort. 29 of them were sent to the battle-field. How many soldiers were left in the fort ?

  = _____ − _____ + _____ = _____ + _____ = [   ]

- There were 688 workers in a factory. 79 workers were dismissed. How many workers were left in the factory ?

  = _____ − _____ + _____ = _____ + _____ = [   ]

- 764 pilgrims are on the way to a shrine. 59 of them are on foot while others are on horses. Find the number of horse-riders.

  = _____ − _____ + _____ = _____ + _____ = [   ]

- 922 sheep were owned by a shepherd. He sold off 69 of them. How many sheep were left with him ?

  = _____ − _____ + _____ = _____ + _____ = [   ]

- A school has 304 students. 19 of them fail the annual examination. Find the number of successful students.

  = _____ − _____ + _____ = _____ + _____ = [   ]

- There were 531 cows in a herd. 39 cows were sold off. How many cows were left behind ?

  = _____ − _____ + _____ = _____ + _____ = [   ]

- 453 labourers worked in a mill. 59 of them went on a strike. Find the number of the remaining workers.

  = _____ − _____ + _____ = _____ + _____ = [   ]

- A cart has 623 pumpkins loaded on it. 79 pumpkins roll off the cart. How many pumpkins are left on the cart ?

  = _____ − _____ + _____ = _____ + _____ = [   ]

(24) ADDING 99 TO NUMERALS

READ CAREFULLY

- Add 100 to the given numeral.
- Then subtract 1 from the new numeral to get the correct sum.

$$275 + 99$$
$$= 275 + 100 - 1$$
$$= 375 - 1 = 374$$
$$275 + 99 = 374$$

DO YOURSELF

A. Do these sums as explained **above** :

- $533 + 99 = 533 + 100 - 1 = 633 - 1 = \boxed{632}$

- $552 + 99 = $ _____ $+$ _____ $-$ _____ $=$ _____ $-$ _____ $=$ ☐

- $286 + 99 = $ _____ $+$ _____ $-$ _____ $=$ _____ $-$ _____ $=$ ☐

- $642 + 99 = $ _____ $+$ _____ $-$ _____ $=$ _____ $-$ _____ $=$ ☐

- $458 + 99 = $ _____ $+$ _____ $-$ _____ $=$ _____ $-$ _____ $=$ ☐

- $823 + 99 = $ _____ $+$ _____ $-$ _____ $=$ _____ $-$ _____ $=$ ☐

- $392 + 99 = $ _____ $+$ _____ $-$ _____ $=$ _____ $-$ _____ $=$ ☐

- $537 + 99 = $ _____ $+$ _____ $-$ _____ $=$ _____ $-$ _____ $=$ ☐

- $143 + 99 = $ _____ $+$ _____ $-$ _____ $=$ _____ $-$ _____ $=$ ☐

- $856 + 99 = $ _____ $+$ _____ $-$ _____ $=$ _____ $-$ _____ $=$ ☐

- $739 + 99 = $ _____ $+$ _____ $-$ _____ $=$ _____ $-$ _____ $=$ ☐

- $377 + 99 = $ _____ $+$ _____ $-$ _____ $=$ _____ $-$ _____ $=$ ☐

- $762 + 99 = $ _____ $+$ _____ $-$ _____ $=$ _____ $-$ _____ $=$ ☐

- $685 + 99 = $ _____ $+$ _____ $-$ _____ $=$ _____ $-$ _____ $=$ ☐

25 SUBTRACTING 99 FROM NUMERALS

- Subtract 100 from the given numeral.

- Then add 1 to the remainder to get the correct result.

$$843 - 99$$
$$= 843 - 100 + 1$$
$$= 743 + 1 = 744$$
$$843 - 99 = 744$$

DO YOURSELF

A. Do these sums as explained above :

❏ $552 - 99 = 552 - 100 + 1 = 452 + 1 = \boxed{453}$

❏ $668 - 99 = $ _____ $- $ _____ $+ $ _____ $= $ _____ $+ $ _____ $= \boxed{}$

❏ $786 - 99 = $ _____ $- $ _____ $+ $ _____ $= $ _____ $+ $ _____ $= \boxed{}$

❏ $498 - 99 = $ _____ $- $ _____ $+ $ _____ $= $ _____ $+ $ _____ $= \boxed{}$

❏ $378 - 99 = $ _____ $- $ _____ $+ $ _____ $= $ _____ $+ $ _____ $= \boxed{}$

❏ $481 - 99 = $ _____ $- $ _____ $+ $ _____ $= $ _____ $+ $ _____ $= \boxed{}$

❏ $596 - 99 = $ _____ $- $ _____ $+ $ _____ $= $ _____ $+ $ _____ $= \boxed{}$

❏ $662 - 99 = $ _____ $- $ _____ $+ $ _____ $= $ _____ $+ $ _____ $= \boxed{}$

❏ $738 - 99 = $ _____ $- $ _____ $+ $ _____ $= $ _____ $+ $ _____ $= \boxed{}$

❏ $344 - 99 = $ _____ $- $ _____ $+ $ _____ $= $ _____ $+ $ _____ $= \boxed{}$

❏ $287 - 99 = $ _____ $- $ _____ $+ $ _____ $= $ _____ $+ $ _____ $= \boxed{}$

❏ $842 - 99 = $ _____ $- $ _____ $+ $ _____ $= $ _____ $+ $ _____ $= \boxed{}$

❏ $938 - 99 = $ _____ $- $ _____ $+ $ _____ $= $ _____ $+ $ _____ $= \boxed{}$

❏ $574 - 99 = $ _____ $- $ _____ $+ $ _____ $= $ _____ $+ $ _____ $= \boxed{}$

Add up following the arrows and write the sum in each square :

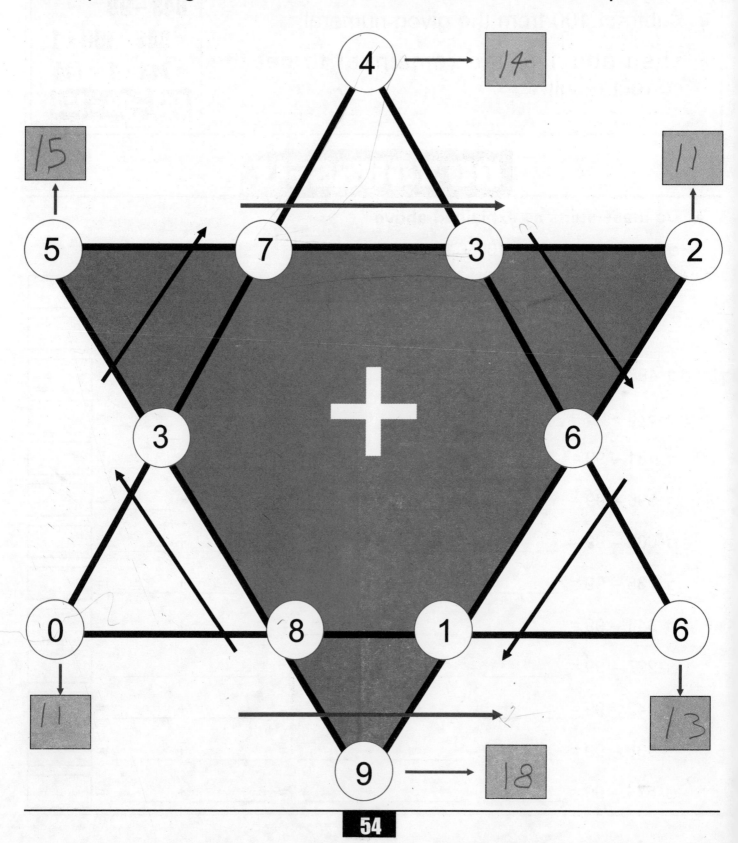

27 ADDITION SWINGS

Fill up each blank to get the total shown in the grey box :

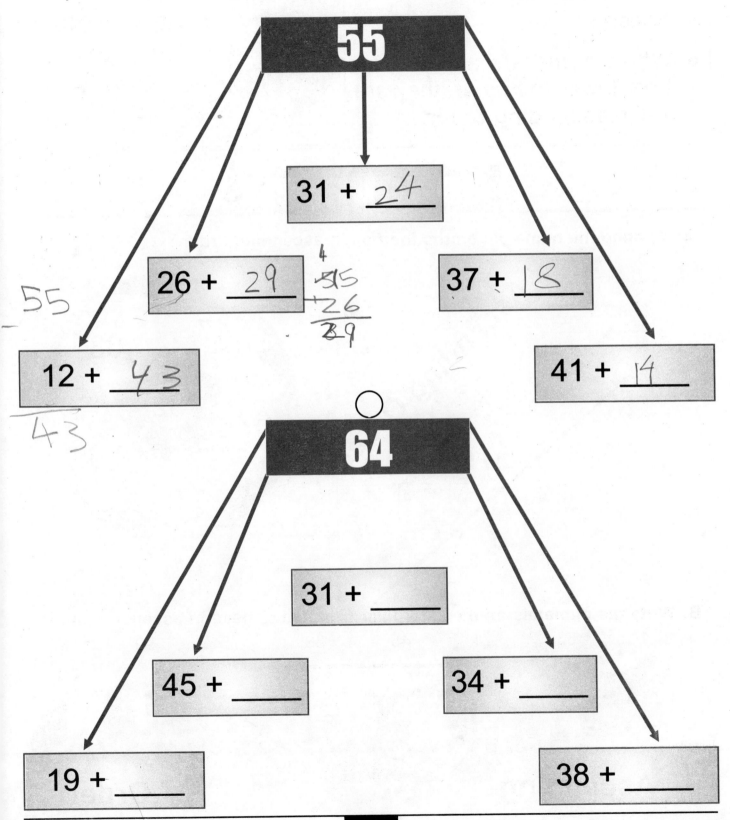

55

31 + 24

26 + 29

37 + 18

12 + 43

41 + 14

55

43

4
55
+26
89

64

31 + ___

45 + ___

34 + ___

19 + ___

38 + ___

28 ASCENDING ORDER

- **Ascend** = go up
- When numerals are written from **lower** to **higher**, they are in the **ascending order**.

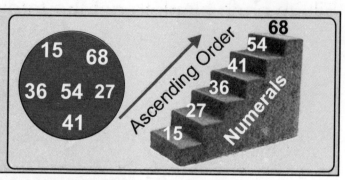

DO YOURSELF

A. Arrange the numerals on the football in **ascending order** :

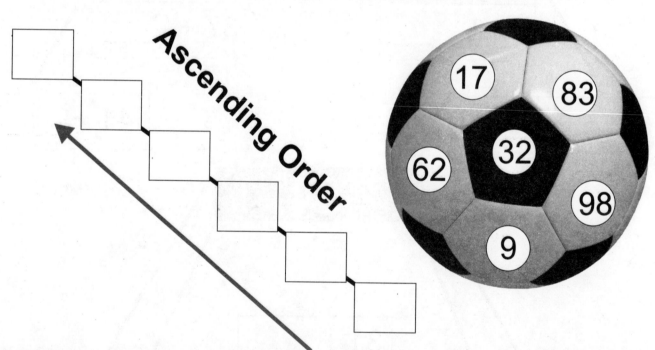

B. Write the numerals on the caterpillar from **tail** to **head** in ascending order :

4   63   21   45   38   75   99   87

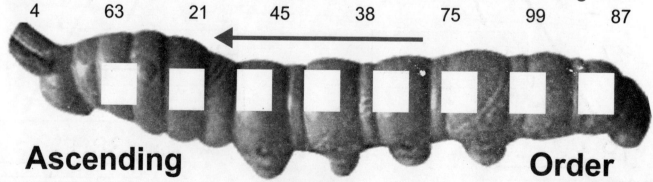

Ascending   **Order**

56

C. Correct the **ascending order** of the numerals :

(a)

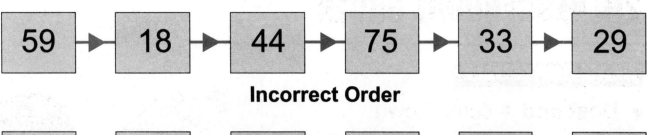

Incorrect Order

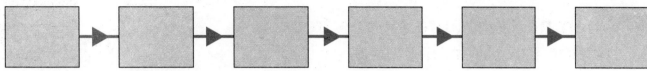

Correct Order

(b)

Incorrect Order

Correct Order

(c)

Incorrect Order

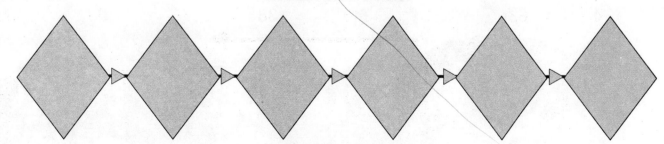

Correct Order

29 DESCENDING ORDER

- **Descend** = come down

- When numerals are written from **higher** to **lower**, they are in the descending order.

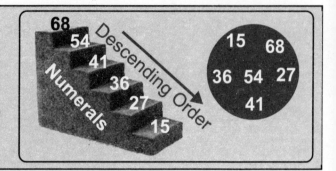

DO YOURSELF

A. Arrange the numbers on the football in **descending order** :

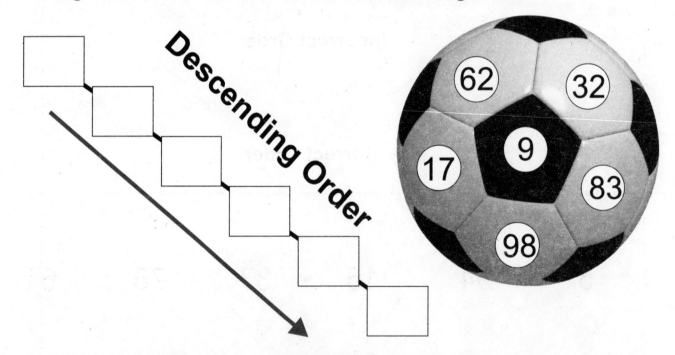

B. Write the numerals on the caterpillar from **head** to **tail in descending order** :

4   63   21   45   38   75   99   87

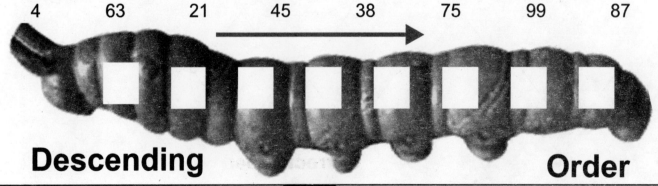

Descending .... **Order**

58

C. Correct the **descending order** of the numerals :

(a)

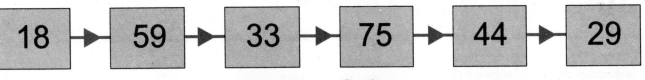

18 → 59 → 33 → 75 → 44 → 29

Incorrect Order

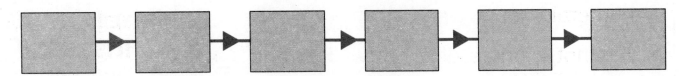

Correct Order

(b)

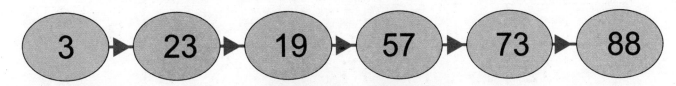

3 → 23 → 19 → 57 → 73 → 88

Incorrect Order

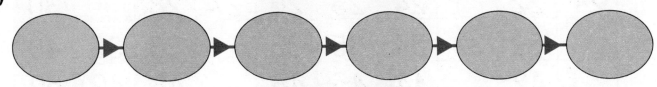

Correct Order

(c)

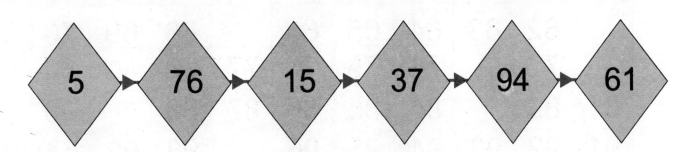

5 → 76 → 15 → 37 → 94 → 61

Incorrect Order

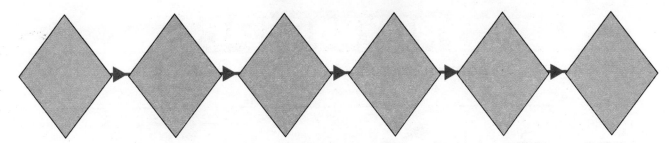

Correct Order

30 PRIME NUMERALS

READ CAREFULLY

- A **prime numeral** cannot be divided by any numeral except **1** and **itself**.

- **1** is not a prime digit but **2, 3, 5** and **7** are prime digits.

> **If a number is not divisible by 2, 3, 5, 7, it is a prime number.**

25 PRIME NUMERALS FROM 1 TO 100

1	2	3	4	5	6	7	8	9	10
11	12	13	14	15	16	17	18	19	20
21	22	23	24	25	26	27	28	29	30
31	32	33	34	35	36	37	38	39	40
41	42	43	44	45	46	47	48	49	50
51	52	53	54	55	56	57	58	59	60
61	62	63	64	65	66	67	68	69	70
71	72	73	74	75	76	77	78	79	80
81	82	83	84	85	86	87	88	89	90
91	92	93	94	95	96	97	98	99	100

DO YOURSELF

Write below the **prime numerals** shown in the above table :

___ ___ ___ ___ ___ ___ ___

___ ___ ___ ___ ___ ___ ___

___ ___ ___ ___

31) MULTIPLICATION : REPEATED ADDITION

READ CAREFULLY

Multiplication means **adding a numeral to itself** many times.

The sign for multiplication is ×.

The numeral after this sign is added to itself.

The numeral before this sign shows the **number of times** to add the other numeral.

The result of multiplication is **product**.

$$3 \times 4 = 3 \text{ times } 4$$
$$= 4 + 4 + 4 = 12$$

$$3 \times 4 = 12$$

DO YOURSELF

A. Multiply by repeated addition :

❑ $5 \times 4 =$ _____ times _____ = [   ] = [   ]

❑ $3 \times 7 =$ _____ times _____ = [   ] = [   ]

❑ $2 \times 4 =$ _____ times _____ = [   ] = [   ]

❑ $5 \times 2 =$ _____ times _____ = [   ] = [   ]

❑ $4 \times 9 =$ _____ times _____ = [   ] = [   ]

❑ $3 \times 6 =$ _____ times _____ = [   ] = [   ]

❑ $5 \times 8 =$ _____ times _____ = [   ] = [   ]

❑ $4 \times 5 =$ _____ times _____ = [   ] = [   ]

B. Write in the multiplication form and find the product :

▢ $2 + 2 + 2 + 2$ = __4__ times __2__ = __4__ × __2__ = **8**

▢ $7 + 7 + 7 + 7 + 7$ = ____ times ____ = ____ × ____ = ☐

▢ $3 + 3 + 3 + 3 + 3 + 3 + 3 + 3$ = ____ times ____ = ____ × ____ = ☐

▢ $4 + 4 + 4 + 4 + 4 + 4 + 4$ = ____ times ____ = ____ × ____ = ☐

▢ $5 + 5 + 5 + 5 + 5$ = ____ times ____ = ____ × ____ = ☐

▢ $6 + 6 + 6 + 6 + 6$ = ____ times ____ = ____ × ____ = ☐

▢ $7 + 7 + 7 + 7 + 7 + 7$ = ____ times ____ = ____ × ____ = ☐

▢ $8 + 8 + 8 + 8 + 8 + 8$ = ____ times ____ = ____ × ____ = ☐

▢ $9 + 9 + 9 + 9 + 9 + 9 + 9$ = ____ times ____ = ____ × ____ = ☐

▢ $10 + 10 + 10 + 10 + 10$ = ____ times ____ = ____ × ____ = ☐

C. Solve these problems mentally :

❑ A grasshopper takes 3 steps in each jump. How many steps will it take in 5 jumps ?

5 times 3 = 5 × 3 = | 3 + 3 + 3 + 3 + 3 | = | **15** |

❑ A deer covers a distance of 2 metres in 1 leap. How many metres will it cover in 4 leaps ?

_____ times _____ = _____ × _____ | | = | |

❑ A child takes 1 minute to walk a distance of 2 metres. How much will the child walk in 6 minutes ?

_____ times _____ = _____ × _____ | | = | |

❑ A snake crawls 3 metres in 1 minute. How much distance will it crawl in 3 minutes ?

_____ times _____ = _____ × _____ | | = | |

❑ A horse runs 8 metres in one minute. How much distance will it run in 4 minutes ?

_____ times _____ = _____ × _____ | | = | |

❑ A cat kills 3 rats daily for its food. How many rats will it have to kill for its food in 6 days ?

_____ times _____ = _____ × _____ | | = | |

❑ A glass needs 3 oranges to be full of juice. How many oranges will be needed to fill 5 such glasses of juice ?

_____ times _____ = _____ × _____ | | = | |

❑ 2 eggs are used to make an omelette. How many eggs shall be needed to make 6 omelettes.

_____ times _____ = _____ × _____ | | = | |

32 MULTIPLICATION BY 2

- 1 time 2 = **2**
- 2 times 2 = 2 + 2 = **4**
- 3 times 2 = 2 + 2 + 2 = **6**
- 4 times 2 = 2 + 2 + 2 + 2 = **8**
- 5 times 2 = 2 + 2 + 2 + 2 + 2 = 10
- 6 times 2 = 2 + 2 + 2 + 2 + 2 + 2 = 12
- 7 times 2 = 2 + 2 + 2 + 2 + 2 + 2 + 2 = 14
- 8 times 2 = 2 + 2 + 2 + 2 + 2 + 2 + 2 + 2 = 16
- 9 times 2 = 2 + 2 + 2 + 2 + 2 + 2 + 2 + 2 + 2 = 18
- 10 times 2 = 2 + 2 + 2 + 2 + 2 + 2 + 2 + 2 + 2 + 2 = 20

1×2	=	2
2×2	=	4
3×2	=	6
4×2	=	8
5×2	=	10
6×2	=	12
7×2	=	14
8×2	=	16
9×2	=	18
10×2	=	20

DO YOURSELF

A. Do these sums mentally :

☐ 8×2
16

☐ 5×2

☐ 10×2

☐ 6×2

☐ 9×2

☐ 7×2

☐ 4×2

☐ 2×2

☐ 3×2

B. Do these problems mentally :

☐ A pumpkin weighs 2 kg. How much will 6 such pumpkins weigh ?

2 kg

= 6 times 2
= 6 × 2
= 12 kg

☐ A car covers 2 km in a minute. What distance will it cover in 10 minutes ?

= ___ times ___
= ___ × ___
= _____ mts.

☐ A bunch has 2 lychees. How many lychees will 5 bunches have ?

= ___ times ___
= ___ × ___
= _____ lychees.

☐ A bottle contains 2 litres of cold drink. How many litres will 4 such bottles contain ?

= ___ times ___
= ___ × ___
= _____ litres.

☐ A button has 2 holes in it. How many holes will 8 such buttons have ?

= ___ times ___
= ___ × ___
= _____ holes.

☐ A watch has 2 hands. How many hands will 9 watches have ?

= ___ times ___
= ___ × ___
= _____ hands.

☐ A man has 2 eyes. How many eyes will 7 men have ?

= ___ times ___
= ___ × ___
= _____ eyes.

☐ A cycle has 2 wheels. How many wheels will 10 cycles have ?

= ___ times ___
= ___ × ___
= _____ wheels.

33 MULTIPLICATION BY 3

READ CAREFULLY

- 1 time 3 = **3**
- 2 times 3 = 3 + 3 = **6**
- 3 times 3 = 3 + 3 + 3 = **9**
- 4 times 3 = 3 + 3 + 3 + 3 = **12**
- 5 times 3 = 3 + 3 + 3 + 3 + 3 = **15**
- 6 times 3 = 3 + 3 + 3 + 3 + 3 + 3 = **18**
- 7 times 3 = 3 + 3 + 3 + 3 + 3 + 3 + 3 = **21**
- 8 times 3 = 3 + 3 + 3 + 3 + 3 + 3 + 3 + 3 = **24**
- 9 times 3 = 3 + 3 + 3 + 3 + 3 + 3 + 3 + 3 + 3 = **27**
- 10 times 3 = 3 + 3 + 3 + 3 + 3 + 3 + 3 + 3 + 3 + 3 = **30**

1×3	=	3
2×3	=	6
3×3	=	9
4×3	=	12
5×3	=	15
6×3	=	18
7×3	=	21
8×3	=	24
9×3	=	27
10×3	=	30

DO YOURSELF

A. Do these sums mentally :

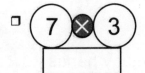

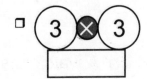

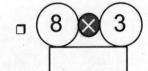

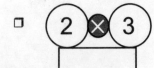

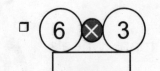

B. Do these problems mentally :

☐ A twig has 3 leaves on it. How many leaves will 6 such twigs have ?

_____ × _____ = _____

☐ A bunch has 3 apricots. How many apricots will 4 bunches have ?

_____ × _____ = _____

☐ A plate has 3 toffees on it. How many toffees will 5 plates have ?

_____ × _____ = _____

☐ 3 biscuits were given to a beggar. How many biscuits will 3 beggars get ?

_____ × _____ = _____

☐ 1 dollar can buy 3 mangoes. How many mangoes will 8 dollars buy ?

_____ × _____ = _____

☐ A T-poy has 3 legs. How many legs will 5 T-poys have ?

_____ × _____ = _____

☐ A fan has 3 wings. How many wings will 9 fans have ?

_____ × _____ = _____

☐ A boy has 3 marbles. How many marbles will 10 boys have ?

_____ × _____ = _____

☐ An auto has 3 wheels. How many wheels will 3 autos have ?

_____ × _____ = _____

☐ A plate has 3 biscuits on it. How many biscuits will 2 such plates have ?

_____ × _____ = _____

34 MULTIPLICATION BY 4

- 1 time $4 = 4$
- 2 times $4 = 4 + 4 = 8$

3 times $4 = 4 + 4 + 4 = 12$

- 4 times $4 = 4 + 4 + 4 + 4 = 16$

5 times $4 = 4 + 4 + 4 + 4 + 4$ $\qquad = 20$

6 times $4 = 4 + 4 + 4 + 4 + 4 + 4$ $\qquad = 24$

7 times $4 = 4 + 4 + 4 + 4 + 4 + 4 + 4$ $\qquad = 28$

8 times $4 = 4 + 4 + 4 + 4 + 4 + 4 + 4 + 4$ $\qquad = 32$

9 times $4 = 4 + 4 + 4 + 4 + 4 + 4 + 4 + 4 + 4$ $\qquad = 36$

- 10 times $4 = 4 + 4 + 4 + 4 + 4 + 4 + 4 + 4 + 4 + 4 = 40$

1×4	=	4
2×4	=	8
3×4	=	12
4×4	=	16
5×4	=	20
6×4	=	24
7×4	=	28
8×4	=	32
9×4	=	36
10×4	=	40

DO YOURSELF

A. Do these sums mentally :

3 ⊗ 4 = 12

10 ⊗ 4 =

2 ⊗ 4 =

7 ⊗ 4 =

9 ⊗ 4 =

8 ⊗ 4 =

6 ⊗ 4 =

5 ⊗ 4 =

4 ⊗ 4 =

B. Do these problems **mentally** :

□ A chair has 4 legs How many legs will 7 chairs have ?

_____ × _____ = _____

□ A bunch has 4 mangoes. How many mangoes will 8 bunches have ?

_____ × _____ = _____

□ A horse has 4 legs. How many legs will 6 horses have ?

_____ × _____ = _____

□ A book costs $ 4. How many dollars will 3 such books cost ?

_____ × _____ = _____

□ 1 man gives 4 toffees to a child. How many toffees will 9 children get ?

_____ × _____ = _____

□ A car has 3 wheels. How many wheels will 4 cars have ?

_____ × _____ = _____

□ A plate has 4 cookies on it. How many cookies will 2 such plates have ?

_____ × _____ = _____

□ There are 4 desks in a row. How many desks will there be in 10 rows ?

_____ × _____ = _____

□ 4 buns were given to a beggar. How many buns will 6 beggars get ?

_____ × _____ = _____

□ A student writes 4 pages in an hour. How many pages will he write in 5 hours ?

_____ × _____ = _____

35 MULTIPLICATION BY 5

READ CAREFULLY

1 time $5 = 5$

• 2 times $5 = 5 + 5 = 10$

3 times $5 = 5 + 5 + 5 = 15$

• 4 times $5 = 5 + 5 + 5 + 5 = 20$

5 times $5 = 5 + 5 + 5 + 5 + 5 = 25$

6 times $5 = 5 + 5 + 5 + 5 + 5 + 5 = 30$

7 times $5 = 5 + 5 + 5 + 5 + 5 + 5 + 5 = 35$

8 times $5 = 5 + 5 + 5 + 5 + 5 + 5 + 5 + 5 = 40$

9 times $5 = 5 + 5 + 5 + 5 + 5 + 5 + 5 + 5 + 5 = 45$

10 times $5 = 5 + 5 + 5 + 5 + 5 + 5 + 5 + 5 + 5 + 5 = 50$

1×5	$=$	5
2×5	$=$	10
3×5	$=$	15
4×5	$=$	20
5×5	$=$	25
6×5	$=$	30
7×5	$=$	35
8×5	$=$	40
9×5	$=$	45
10×5	$=$	50

DO YOURSELF

A. Do these sums mentally :

☐ (9 ⊗ 5)
45

☐ (4 ⊗ 5)

☐ (8 ⊗ 5)

☐ (6 ⊗ 5)

☐ (5 ⊗ 5)

☐ (7 ⊗ 4)

☐ (3 ⊗ 5)

☐ (10 ⊗ 5)

☐ (2 ⊗ 5)

B. Do these problems mentally :

▫ A plate has 5 biscuits on it. How many biscuits will 7 such plates have ?

_____ × _____ = _____

▫ A bunch has 5 lychees. How many lychees will 6 bunches have ?

_____ × _____ = _____

▫ A pentagon has 5 sides. How many sides will 9 pentagons have ?

_____ × _____ = _____

▫ A hand has 5 fingers. How many fingers will 2 hands have ?

_____ × _____ = _____

▫ 1 dollar can buy 5 note-books. How many note-books will 3 dollars buy ?

_____ × _____ = _____

▫ There are 5 seats on a bench. How many seats will 5 such benches have ?

_____ × _____ = _____

▫ A hen bore 5 chicks. How many chicks will 4 hens bear ?

_____ × _____ = _____

▫ A boy can write 5 pages in an hour. How many pages will he write in 8 hours ?

_____ × _____ = _____

▫ 5 coins are given to a beggar. How many coins will be given to 3 beggars ?

_____ × _____ = _____

▫ A worker earns $ 5 a day. How much will he earn in 10 days ?

_____ × _____ = _____

36 MULTIPLICATION BY 6

- 1 time   6 = 6
- 2 times 6 = 6 + 6 = 12
- 3 times 6 = 6 + 6 + 6 = 18
- 4 times 6 = 6 + 6 + 6 + 6 = 24
- 5 times 6 = 6 + 6 + 6 + 6 + 6 = 30
- 6 times 6 = 6 + 6 + 6 + 6 + 6 + 6 = 36
- 7 times 6 = 6 + 6 + 6 + 6 + 6 + 6 + 6 = 42
- 8 times 6 = 6 + 6 + 6 + 6 + 6 + 6 + 6 + 6 = 48
- 9 times 6 = 6 + 6 + 6 + 6 + 6 + 6 + 6 + 6 + 6 = 54
- 10 times 6 = 6 + 6 + 6 + 6 + 6 + 6 + 6 + 6 + 6 + 6 = 60

1×6	=	6
2×6	=	12
3×6	=	18
4×6	=	24
5×6	=	30
6×6	=	36
7×6	=	42
8×6	=	48
9×6	=	54
10×6	=	60

DO YOURSELF

A. Do these sums mentally :

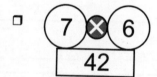

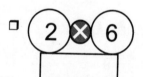

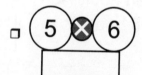

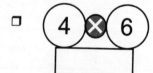

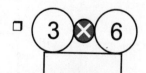

B. Do these problems **mentally** :

□ A man earns $ 6 a day. How much will he earn in 7 days ?

_____ × _____ = _____

□ A flower has 6 petals. How many petals will 8 such flowers have ?

_____ × _____ = _____

□ A man works 6 days a week. How many days will he work in 9 weeks ?

_____ × _____ = _____

□ An apple is cut into 6 pieces. How many pieces will 7 apples be cut into ?

_____ × _____ = _____

□ There are 6 desks in a row ? How many desks will 4 such rows have ?

_____ × _____ = _____

□ An insect has 6 legs. How many legs will 10 insects have ?

_____ × _____ = _____

□ There are 6 leaves on a twig. How many leaves will 2 twigs have ?

_____ × _____ = _____

□ A bunch has 6 lychees. How many lychees will 3 such bunches have ?

_____ × _____ = _____

□ 6 slices of bread are given to a beggar. How many slices will 6 beggars get ?

_____ × _____ = _____

□ A shirt needs 6 buttons. How many buttons will 5 shirts need ?

_____ × _____ = _____

READ CAREFULLY

- 1 time   7 = 7
- 2 times 7 = 7 + 7 = 14
- 3 times 7 = 7 + 7 + 7 = 21
- 4 times 7 = 7 + 7 + 7 + 7 = 28
- 5 times 7 = 7 + 7 + 7 + 7 + 7 = 35
- 6 times 7 = 7 + 7 + 7 + 7 + 7 + 7 = 42
- 7 times 7 = 7 + 7 + 7 + 7 + 7 + 7 + 7   = 49
- 8 times 7 = 7 + 7 + 7 + 7 + 7 + 7 + 7 + 7 = 56
- 9 times 7 = 7 + 7 + 7 + 7 + 7 + 7 + 7 + 7 + 7 = 63
- 10 times 7 = 7 + 7 + 7 + 7 + 7 + 7 + 7 + 7 + 7 + 7 = 70

1 × 7	=	7
2 × 7	=	14
3 × 7	=	21
4 × 7	=	28
5 × 7	=	35
6 × 7	=	42
7 × 7	=	49
8 × 7	=	56
9 × 7	=	63
10 × 7	=	70

DO YOURSELF

A. Do these sums mentally :

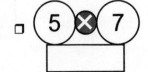

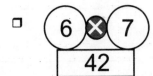

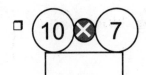

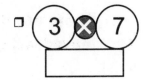

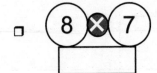

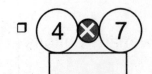

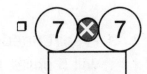

B. Do these problems mentally :

- ❑ A week has 7 days. How many days are there in 4 weeks ?

  _____ × _____ = _____

- ❑ There are 7 toffees on a plate. How many toffees will be there on 5 such plates ?

  _____ × _____ = _____

- ❑ A bunch has 7 lychees. How many lychees will 2 such bunches have ?

  _____ × _____ = _____

- ❑ An apple is cut into 7 pieces. How many pieces will 8 apples be cut into ?

  _____ × _____ = _____

- ❑ There are 7 children in a row ? How many children will 3 such rows have ?

  _____ × _____ = _____

- ❑ There are 7 petals in a flower. How many petals will 7 such flowers have ?

  _____ × _____ = _____

- ❑ A hen lays 7 eggs daily. How many eggs will it lay in 8 days ?

  _____ × _____ = _____

- ❑ A school has 7 periods daily. How many periods will it have in 6 days ?

  _____ × _____ = _____

- ❑ 7 coins are given to a beggar. How many coins will 10 beggars get ?

  _____ × _____ = _____

- ❑ A shirt has 7 buttons. How many buttons will 9 shirts have ?

  _____ × _____ = _____

㊳ MULTIPLICATION BY 8

READ CAREFULLY

- 1 time   8 = 8
- 3 times 8 = 8 + 8 + 8 = 24
- 5 times 8 = 8 + 8 + 8 + 8 + 8 = 40
- 6 times 8 = 8 + 8 + 8 + 8 + 8 + 8 = 48
- 7 times 8 = 8 + 8 + 8 + 8 + 8 + 8 + 8   = 56
- 8 times 8 = 8 + 8 + 8 + 8 + 8 + 8 + 8 + 8 = 64
- 9 times 8 = 8 + 8 + 8 + 8 + 8 + 8 + 8 + 8 + 8 = 72
- 10 times 8 = 8 + 8 + 8 + 8 + 8 + 8 + 8 + 8 + 8 + 8 = 80

- 2 times 8 = 8 + 8 = 16
- 4 times 8 = 8 + 8 + 8 + 8 = 32

1 × 8	=	8
2 × 8	=	16
3 × 8	=	24
4 × 8	=	32
5 × 8	=	40
6 × 8	=	48
7 × 8	=	56
8 × 8	=	64
9 × 8	=	72
10 × 8	=	80

DO YOURSELF

A. Do these sums mentally :

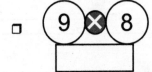

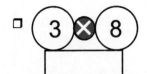

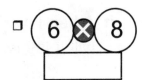

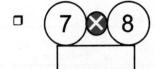

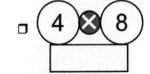

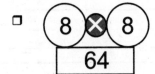

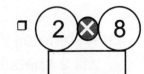

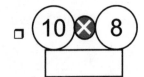

B. Do these problems mentally :

- A spider has 8 legs. How many legs will 7 spiders have ?

  _____ × _____ = _____

- An octagon has 8 sides. How many sides will 4 octagons have ?

  _____ × _____ = _____

- An office opens for 8 hours a day. For how many hours will it open in 6 days.

  _____ × _____ = _____

- A school has 8 periods daily. How many periods will it have in 5 days ?

  _____ × _____ = _____

- A bunch has 8 lychees on it. How many lychees will 8 such bunches have ?

  _____ × _____ = _____

- There are 8 desks in a row. How many desks will there be in 3 rows ?

  _____ × _____ = _____

- There are 8 passengers in a boat. How many passengers will 9 such boats have ?

  _____ × _____ = _____

- A dance group has 8 girls. How many girls will 2 such group have ?

  _____ × _____ = _____

- A bread is cut into 8 slices. How many slices will 10 breads be cut into ?

  _____ × _____ = _____

- There are 8 shops on 1 floor of a Mall. How many shops will there be on 3 floors ?

  _____ × _____ = _____

READ CAREFULLY

- 1 time   9 = **9**
- 2 times 9 = 9 + 9 = **18**
- 3 times 9 = 9 + 9 + 9 = **27**
- 4 times 9 = 9 + 9 + 9 + 9 = **36**
- 5 times 9 = 9 + 9 + 9 + 9 + 9 = **45**
- 6 times 9 = 9 + 9 + 9 + 9 + 9 + 9 = **54**
- 7 times 9 = 9 + 9 + 9 + 9 + 9 + 9 + 9 = **63**
- 8 times 9 = 9 + 9 + 9 + 9 + 9 + 9 + 9 + 9 = **72**
- 9 times 9 = 9 + 9 + 9 + 9 + 9 + 9 + 9 + 9 + 9 = **81**
- 10 times 9 = 9 + 9 + 9 + 9 + 9 + 9 + 9 + 9 + 9 + 9 = **90**

1 × 9	=	9
2 × 9	=	18
3 × 9	=	27
4 × 9	=	36
5 × 9	=	45
6 × 9	=	54
7 × 9	=	63
8 × 9	=	72
9 × 9	=	81
10 × 9	=	90

DO YOURSELF

A. Do these sums mentally :

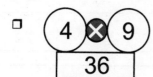

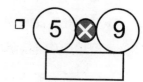

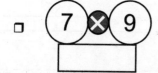
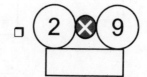

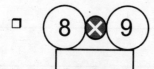

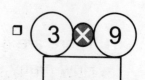

B. Do these problems **mentally** :

❏ A rose bush has 9 flowers. How many flowers will 5 such bushes have ?

_____ × _____ = _____

❏ There are 9 eggs in a nest. How many eggs will there be in 6 nests ?

_____ × _____ = _____

❏ 9 labourers can reap a field. How many labourers will reap 5 such fields ?

_____ × _____ = _____

❏ 9 birds are sitting on a tree-branch. How many birds will sit on 7 such branches ?

_____ × _____ = _____

❏ A batsman got 9 runs in an over. How many runs will he get in 8 overs ?

_____ × _____ = _____

❏ 9 beggars were sitting in a row. How many beggars will there be in 9 rows ?

_____ × _____ = _____

❏ John wins 9 marbles in a game. How many marbles will he win in 4 games ?

_____ × _____ = _____

❏ A police party has 9 policemen. How many policemen will 10 such parties have ?

_____ × _____ = _____

❏ 9 dollars are needed to buy a toy-car. How many dollars will be needed for 3 toy-cars ?

_____ × _____ = _____

❏ A kabaddi team has 9 players. How many players will there be in 2 such teams ?

_____ × _____ = _____

⑳ MULTIPLICATION BY 10

- 1 time 10 = 10
- 2 times 10 = 10 + 10 = 20
- 3 times 10 = 10 + 10 + 10 = 30
- 4 times 10 = 10 + 10 + 10 + 10 = 40
- 5 times 10 = 10 + 10 + 10 + 10 + 10 = 50
- 6 times 10 = 10 + 10 + 10 + 10 + 10 + 10 = 60
- 7 times 10 = 10 + 10 + 10 + 10 + 10 + 10 + 10 = 70
- 8 times 10 = 9 + 9 + 9 + 9 + 9 + 9 + 9 + 9 = 80
- 9 times 10 = 9 + 9 + 9 + 9 + 9 + 9 + 9 + 9 + 9 = 90
- 10 times 10 = 9 + 9 + 9 + 9 + 9 + 9 + 9 + 9 + 9 + 9 = 100

1 × 10 =	10
2 × 10 =	20
3 × 10 =	30
4 × 10 =	40
5 × 10 =	50
6 × 10 =	60
7 × 10 =	70
8 × 10 =	80
9 × 10 =	90
10 × 10 =	100

DO YOURSELF

A. Do these sums mentally :

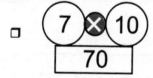

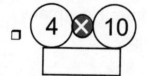

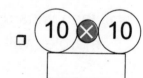

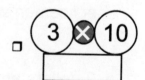

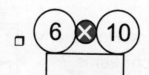

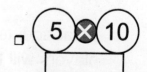

B. Do these problems mentally :

- A classroom has 10 desks in a row. How many desks will there be in 4 rows ?

_____ × _____ = _____

- 10 toffees are given to a child. How many toffees will be given to 9 children ?

_____ × _____ = _____

- A decagon has 10 angles. How many angles will 10 decagons have ?

_____ × _____ = _____

- A garland has 10 rose-flowers. How many flowers will 5 such garlands have ?

_____ × _____ = _____

- There are 10 pearls in a ring ? How many pearls will 8 such rings have ?

_____ × _____ = _____

- There are 10 grapes in a bunch. How many grapes will 9 such bunches have ?

_____ × _____ = _____

- There are 10 joints on a sugarcane. How many joints will 3 sugar-canes have ?

_____ × _____ = _____

- A man has 10 fingers. How many fingers will 6 men have ?

_____ × _____ = _____

- A lady has 10 toes. How many toes will 7 ladies have ?

_____ × _____ = _____

- A bunch has 10 bananas on it. How many bananas will 2 such bunches have ?

_____ × _____ = _____

41 DIVISION : REPEATED SUBTRACTION

- The word—**division**—means sharing equally. Its sign is $\div$.

- Division means making equal groups out of a numeral called dividend.

- It can be done by subtracting a smaller numeral (**divisor**) again and again from the dividend.

- The numeral of times subtraction can be done gives the result of the division.

- The result of division is called **quotient**.

$8 \div 2$
$= 8 - 2 - 2 - 2 - 2 = 0$
$= 4$ times subtraction of 2 from 8.
$\therefore 8 \div 2 = 4$

8 is the DIVIDEND
2 is the DIVISOR
4 is the QUOTIENT

DIVISION IS OPPOSITE OF MULTIPLICATION.

DO YOURSELF

A. Divide by repeated subtraction :

$10 \div 2 =$	$10 - 2 - 2 - 2 - 2 - 2 = 0$	$= 5$ times subtraction $=$	5
$9 \div 3 =$		$= \underline{\quad}$ times subtraction $=$	
$12 \div 4 =$		$= \underline{\quad}$ times subtraction $=$	
$15 \div 3 =$		$= \underline{\quad}$ times subtraction $=$	
$16 \div 4 =$		$= \underline{\quad}$ times subtraction $=$	
$18 \div 6 =$		$= \underline{\quad}$ times subtraction $=$	
$30 \div 6 =$		$= \underline{\quad}$ times subtraction $=$	

B. Do these problems mentally :

- A man had 21 toffees. He decided to give them to 7 children. How many toffees will each child get ?

  ____ ÷ ____ [   ] = ____ times subtraction = [   ]

- A baker has 24 cookies. He places 6 cookies in a plate. How many plates will be needed for all the cookies ?

  ____ ÷ ____ [   ] = ____ times subtraction = [   ]

- There are 35 lychees on some bunches. If each bunch has 7 lychees, how many bunches are there ?

  ____ ÷ ____ [   ] = ____ times subtraction = [   ]

- 27 bananas are needed for worship. If a bunch contains 9 bananas, how many bunches will be needed for the worship ?

  ____ ÷ ____ [   ] = ____ times subtraction = [   ]

- There are 40 marbles with some children. If each child has 8 marbles, how many children are there ?

  ____ ÷ ____ [   ] = ____ times subtraction = [   ]

- There are 21 biscuits with a baker. He wants to give them to 7 beggars. How many biscuits will each beggar get ?

  ____ ÷ ____ [   ] = ____ times subtraction = [   ]

- The total number of legs of some spiders is 32. If each spider has 8 legs, how many spiders are there ?

  ____ ÷ ____ [   ] = ____ times subtraction = [   ]

- 15 ice-cream cones were distributed among children. If each child gets 3 ice-cream cones, how many children are there ?

  ____ ÷ ____ [   ] = ____ times subtraction = [   ]

- 10 candies were distributed among children. If each child gets 2 candies, how many children are there ?

  ____ ÷ ____ [   ] = ____ times subtraction = [   ]

42 DIVISION BY GROUPING

READ CAREFULLY

- Instead of the repeated subtraction, division can also be done in another method.

- This method finds **how many groups** of the divisor are contained in the dividend.

- Everything else is the same as in the method of repeated subtraction.

- 30 balls shown in front are made into 6 groups of 5 each.

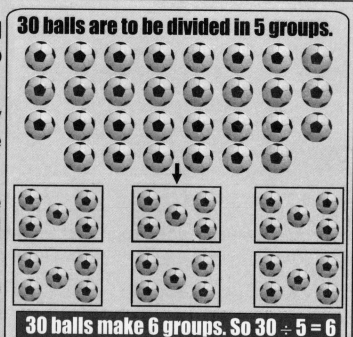

30 balls are to be divided in 5 groups.

30 balls make 6 groups. So 30 ÷ 5 = 6

DO YOURSELF

A. Make groups and divide :

▫ 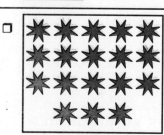 ÷ 5 = ☐ ☐ ☐ = ___ groups

15 ÷ 5 = ___

▫ ÷ 3 = ☐ ☐ ☐ ☐ = ___ groups

12 ÷ 3 = ___

▫ 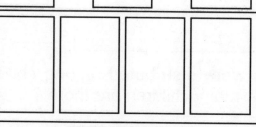 ÷ 6 = = ___ groups

18 ÷ 6 = ___

B. Do these problems **mentally** :

- A man had 18 marbles. He decided to give them to 6 children. How many marbles will each child get ?

  _____ marbles = _____ groups = _____ marbles each

- A shepherd has 36 sheep. He wants to divide them among his 4 sons. How many sheep will each son get ?

  _____ sheep = _____ groups = _____ sheep each

- A rich man has 48 coins. He wants to give them to 8 beggars. How many coins will each beggar get ?

  _____ coins = _____ groups = _____ coins each

- A baker bakes 63 biscuits. He wants to distribute them among 9 children. How many biscuits will each child get ?

  _____ biscuits = _____ groups = _____ biscuits each

- A king buys 27 blankets for poor old men. He gives 1 blanket to each old man. How many old men are there ?

  _____ old men = _____ groups = _____ old men

- 81 mangoes were distributed among some men. 9 mangoes were given to each man. How many men were there ?

  _____ mangoes = _____ groups = _____ men

- 72 pumpkins were placed in some baskets. If 8 pumpkins are there in each basket. Find the number of baskets ?

  _____ pumpkins = _____ groups = _____ baskets

- 60 lychees are there on some bunches. If each bunch has 6 lychees, find the number of bunches ?

  _____ lychees = _____ groups = _____ bunches

- A man reads 45 pages of a book in one day. If he reads 5 pages per hour, how many hours will he take to read all the pages ?

  _____ pages = _____ groups = _____ hours

- A farmer's hen lays 4 eggs every day. In how many days will the hen lay 32 eggs ?

  _____ eggs = _____ groups = _____ days

READ CAREFULLY

- Division is the opposite of multiplication.

- So multiplication tables can be used for division.

- Think over the divisor's multiplication table to reach the dividend.

- The number of last step to reach the dividend will be the quotient of division.

- In $42 \div 7$ _____

- 7 is the **divisor** and 42 is the **dividend**

- We know that in multiplication table of seven, $7 \times 6 = 42$.

- Clearly, the **6th step reaches the** dividend 42.

- So 6 is the **quotient**.

  $42 \div 7 = 6$

DO YOURSELF

A. Solve these sums using multiplication tables :

▢ $48 \div 6$

We know that $6 \times 8 = 48$. So 8 is the quotient.

▢ $54 \div 9$

We know that _____ × _____ = _____ . So _____ is the quotient.

▢ $63 \div 9$

We know that _____ × _____ = _____ . So _____ is the quotient.

▢ $50 \div 5$

We know that _____ × _____ = _____ . So _____ is the quotient.

▢ $32 \div 4$

We know that _____ × _____ = _____ . So _____ is the quotient.

❑ 18 ÷ 3

We know that _____ × _____ = _____ . So _____ is the quotient.

❑ 16 ÷ 8

We know that _____ × _____ = _____ . So _____ is the quotient.

❑ 12 ÷ 2

We know that _____ × _____ = _____ . So _____ is the quotient.

❑ 42 ÷ 7

We know that _____ × _____ = _____ . So _____ is the quotient.

❑ 56 ÷ 7

We know that _____ × _____ = _____ . So _____ is the quotient.

❑ 81 ÷ 9

We know that _____ × _____ = _____ . So _____ is the quotient.

❑ 72 ÷ 8

We know that _____ × _____ = _____ . So _____ is the quotient.

❑ 35 ÷ 5

We know that _____ × _____ = _____ . So _____ is the quotient.

❑ 24 ÷ 4

We know that _____ × _____ = _____ . So _____ is the quotient.

❑ 36 ÷ 9

We know that _____ × _____ = _____ . So _____ is the quotient.

❑ 70 ÷ 7

We know that _____ × _____ = _____ . So _____ is the quotient.

❑ 64 ÷ 8

We know that _____ × _____ = _____ . So _____ is the quotient.

❑ 49 ÷ 7

We know that _____ × _____ = _____ . So _____ is the quotient.

B. Solve these division sums mentally :

- $9 \div 3 = \boxed{}$
- $10 \div 5 = \boxed{}$
- $12 \div 6 = \boxed{}$
- $6 \div 2 = \boxed{}$
- $8 \div 4 = \boxed{}$
- $54 \div 6 = \boxed{}$
- $42 \div 7 = \boxed{}$
- $36 \div 9 = \boxed{}$
- $4 \div 2 = \boxed{}$
- $45 \div 5 = \boxed{}$
- $40 \div 8 = \boxed{}$
- $32 \div 8 = \boxed{}$
- $14 \div 2 = \boxed{}$
- $20 \div 4 = \boxed{}$
- $18 \div 6 = \boxed{}$

- $16 \div 2 = \boxed{}$
- $24 \div 4 = \boxed{}$
- $28 \div 7 = \boxed{}$
- $35 \div 5 = \boxed{}$
- $81 \div 9 = \boxed{}$
- $64 \div 8 = \boxed{}$
- $72 \div 9 = \boxed{}$
- $70 \div 7 = \boxed{}$
- $48 \div 8 = \boxed{}$
- $48 \div 7 = \boxed{}$
- $50 \div 5 = \boxed{}$
- $40 \div 4 = \boxed{}$
- $21 \div 3 = \boxed{}$
- $30 \div 3 = \boxed{}$
- $60 \div 6 = \boxed{}$

READ CAREFULLY

- When two straight lines meet at a **point**, an angle is formed.

- Angles are measured in **degrees**.

- We use a **protractor** to measure angles.

- Angles are named using capital letters.

- The letter where the angle is formed is written in the middle.

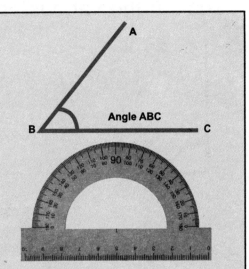

A **circle** has an angle of 360 degrees (360°) at its centre.

A **semi-circle** has an angle of 180 degrees (180°) at its centre.

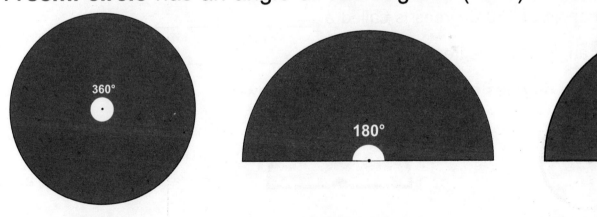

CIRCLE   SEMI-CIRCLE   QUADRANT

A **quadrant** (one-fourth of a circle) has an angle of 90 degrees (90°) at its centre.

An angle of 90° is called a RIGHT ANGLE.

An angle of 180° is called a STRAIGHT ANGLE.

An angle of 360° is called a CIRCLE.

An angle smaller than 90° is called an ACUTE ANGLE.

An angle larger than 90° is called an OBTUSE ANGLE.

Look at the various angles shown below :

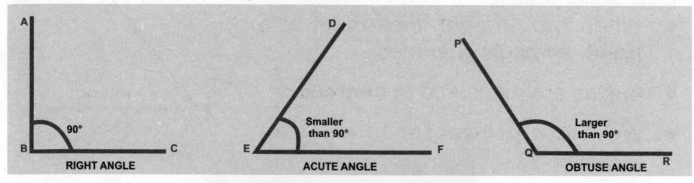

DO YOURSELF

A. Fill up each blank :

❏ An angle is formed when two straight lines meet at a _____ .

❏ A circle is an angle of _____ and a semi-circle is of _____ .

❏ A quadrant (one-fourth of a circle) is an angle of _____ .

❏ An angle of 180 degrees is called a _____ .

❏ An angle of 90 degrees is called a _____ .

B. Write the degrees of each angle shown below :

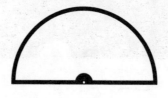

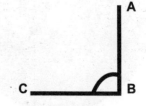

_____   _____   _____

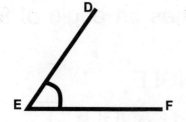

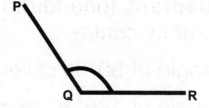

_____   _____

(45) TRIANGLES

- A **triangle** is a figure bounded by three sides.

- Three sides of a triangle meet at three points forming angles.

- So a triangle has three angles.

- According to angles, triangles are of three types.

- According to sides, triangles are of three types as well.

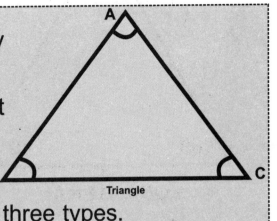

Triangle

A. According to **angles**, triangles are of three types :

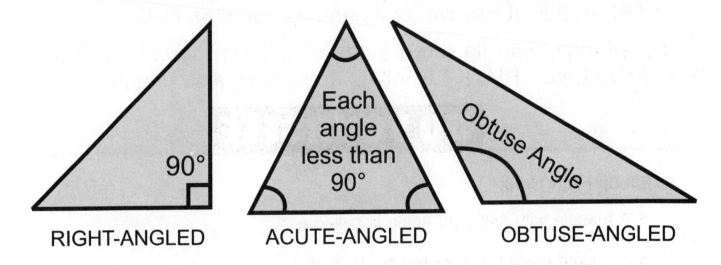

RIGHT-ANGLED   ACUTE-ANGLED   OBTUSE-ANGLED

- ☐ A triangle which has one of its angle to be of **90°** is called a RIGHT-ANGLED TRIANGLE.

- ☐ A triangle which has each of its angles **smaller than 90°** is called an ACUTE-ANGLED TRIANGLE.

- ☐ A triangle which has one of its angles to be **larger than 90°** is called an OBTUSE-ANGLED TRIANGLE.

B. According to **sides**, triangles are of three types :

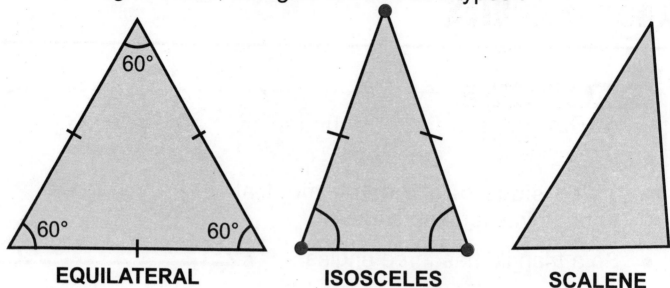

| EQUILATERAL | ISOSCELES | SCALENE |

❏ A triangle with all its sides equal is called an EQUILATERAL TRIANGLE. It has all its angles equal as well. So it is called an EQUIANGULAR TRIANGLE also.

❏ A triangle with two equal sides is called an ISOSCELES TRIANGLE. It has two of its angles equal as well.

❏ A triangle with its three sides of different lengths is called a SCALENE TRIANGLE. All its angles are also unequal.

DO YOURSELF

A. Fill up each blank :

❏ A triangle with one right angle is called a_____ .

❏ An acute-angled triangle has all its angles _____ than 90°.

❏ An obtuse-angled triangle has one of its angles _____ than 90°.

❏ A triangle with all its sides unequal is a _____ triangle.

❏ A triangle with all its sides equal is an _____ triangle.

❏ A triangle with two its sides equal is an _____ triangle.

B. Name each triangle shown below :

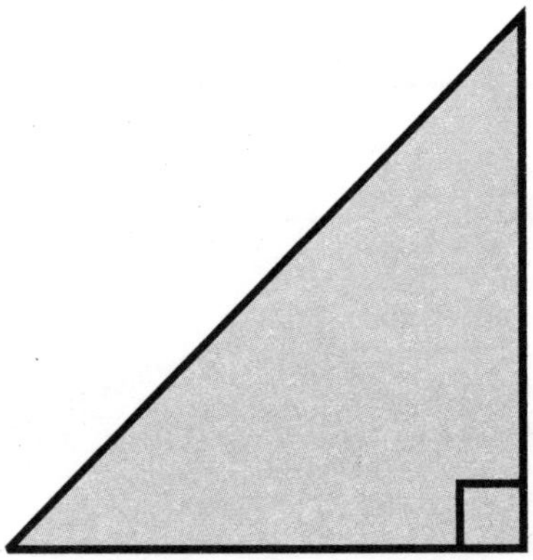

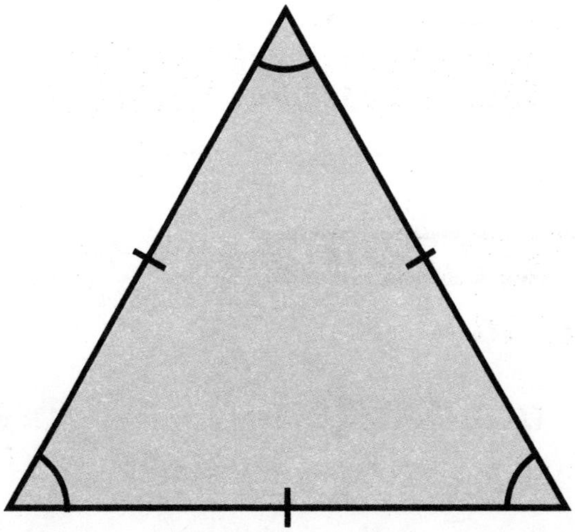

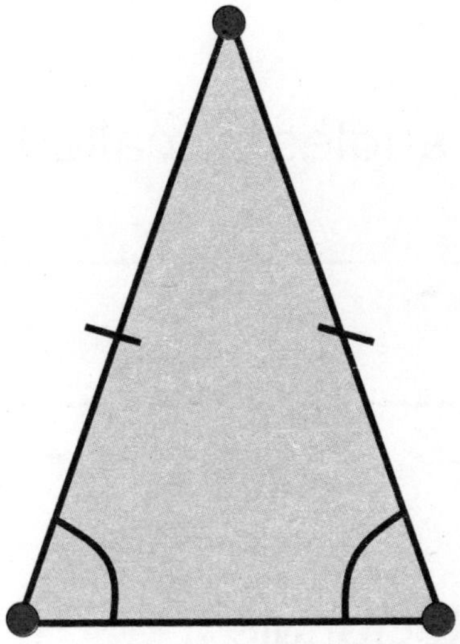

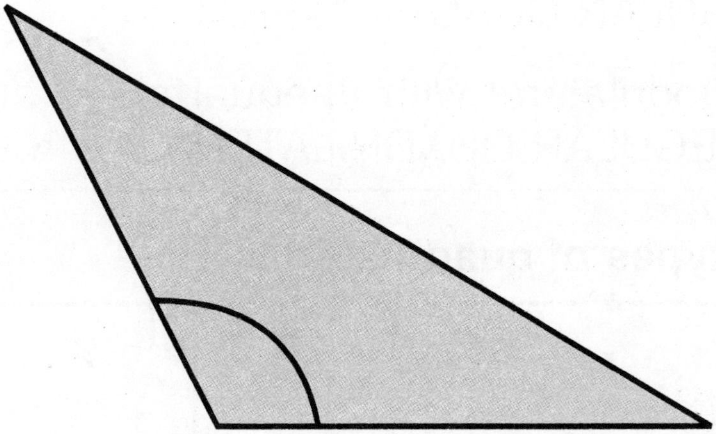

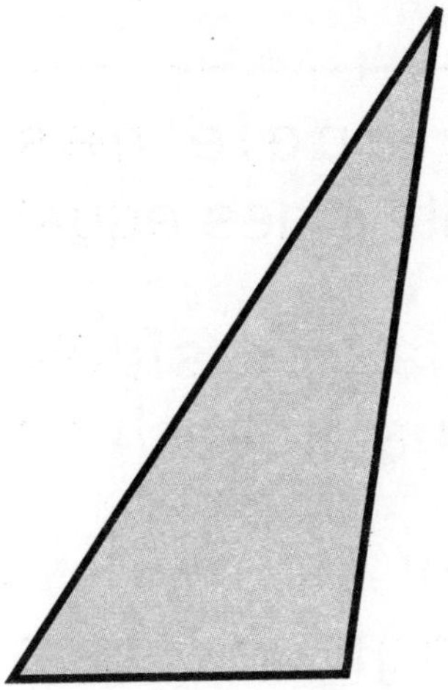

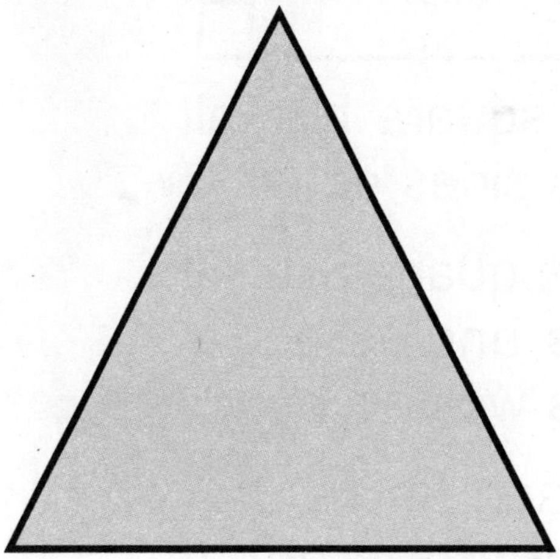

_____

_____

_____

_____

_____

_____

46 QUADRILATERALS

READ CAREFULLY

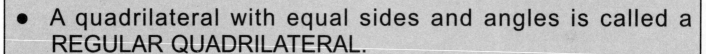

- **Quad** means **four**.

- A **quadrilateral** is a figure bounded by four sides.

- Four sides of a quadrilateral meet at four points forming angles.

- A quadrilateral with equal sides and angles is called a REGULAR QUADRILATERAL.

- A quadrilateral with unequal sides and angles is called an IRREGULAR QUADRILATERAL.

Six types of quadrilaterals :

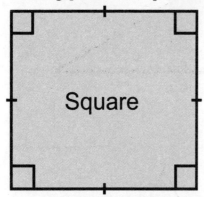

Square

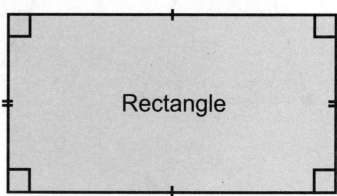

Rectangle

- ❑ A square has all its sides equal.

- ❑ A square has all its angles equal as well.

- ❑ Each angle of a square is equal to 90°.

- ❑ A rectangle has its opposite sides equal.

- ❑ Its adjacent sides are not equal to each other.

- ❑ Each of the angles of a rectangle is equal to 90°.

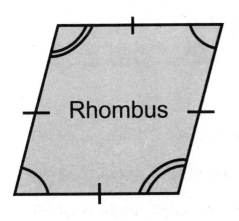

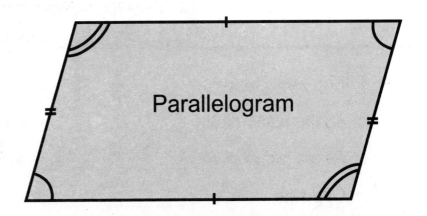

- [ ] A rhombus has all its sides equal.

- [ ] A rhombus has its opposite sides parallel as well.

- [ ] A rhombus has its opposite angles equal.

- [ ] A parallelogram has its opposite sides equal.

- [ ] Its adjacent sides are not equal in length.

- [ ] Its opposite angles are equal as well.

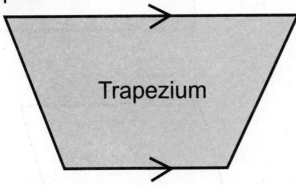

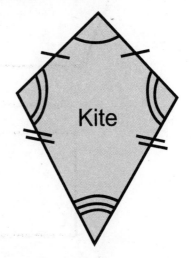

- [ ] A trapezium has two of its sides parallel.

- [ ] These parallel sides are not equal.

- [ ] A trapezium is called a trapezoid also.

- [ ] A kite has two pairs of equal adjacent sides.

- [ ] It has one pair of opposite angles equal.

- [ ] But the other pair of opposite angles are unequal.

DO YOURSELF

A. Fill up each blank :

- All the sides of a _____ are equal and each angle is of 90°.

- All the sides of a _____ are equal but no angle is of 90°.

- Opposite sides of a _____ are equal and each angle is of 90°.

- A _____ has two pairs of its adjacent sides equal.

- A _____ has two of its sides parallel but unequal.

- A _____ has its opposite sides equal but no angle equal to 90°.

B. Name each quadrilateral shown below :

_____   _____

_____   _____

_____   _____

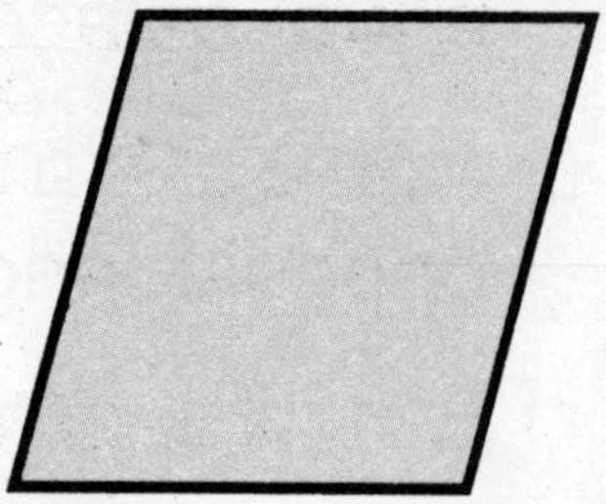

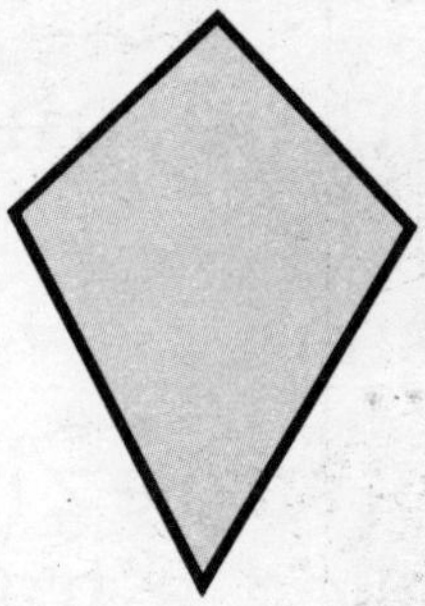